The Institute of Biology's
Studies in Biology

The Biology of Helminth Parasites

Kathleen M. Lyons

Edward Arnold

First published 1978
by Edward Arnold (Publishers) Limited
41 Bedford Square, London, WC1B 3DQ

ISBN: 0 7131 2715 5

British Library Cataloguing in Publication Data

Lyons, Kathleen M
The biology of helminth parasites
– (Institute of Biology. Studies in biology;
no. 102; 0537-9024).
1. Worms, Intestinal and parasitic
I. Title II. Series
595'.1'04524 QL392

ISBN 0-7131-2715-5

Printed and bound in Great Britain at
The Camelot Press Ltd, Southampton

General Preface to the Series

Because it is no longer possible for one textbook to cover the whole field of biology while remaining sufficiently up to date the Institute of Biology has sponsored this series so that teachers and students can learn about significant developments. The enthusiastic acceptance of 'Studies in Biology' shows that the books are providing authoritative views of biological topics.

The features of the series include the attention given to methods, the selected list of books for further reading and, wherever possible, suggestions for practical work.

Readers' comments will be welcomed by the Education Officer of the Institute.

1979

Institute of Biology
41 Queen's Gate
London SW7 5HU

Preface

Helminth parasites have representatives from three completely different phyla of invertebrates: the platyhelminths, the acanthocephalans and the nematodes. Despite their different origins these helminths face similar problems in their life styles as parasites and show a remarkable amount of convergence in their adaptations to parasitism. The purpose of this book is to challenge the general assumption that parasites live a life of luxury and ease in association with their hosts, and to examine some of the problems helminths have to face, and some of the often remarkable answers to these problems that they have evolved. The fact that the host-parasite relationship is a dynamic one and perpetually changing means that parasites are constantly evolving improved relationships with their hosts. Studying the ways in which they do this leads us into the realms of structural, physiological, immunological and behavioural adaptations as well as to the underlying genetic causes and evolutionary routes. This account aims to summarize recent findings in these fields of helminth biology in a compact form and to use this information to show how effectively helminth parasites are adapted to their very demanding and specialized ways of life.

Bryanston School,
Blandford Forum, Dorset, 1978

K. M. L.

Contents

1 Introduction

The helminths are parasitic worms belonging to three different groups of invertebrates: the platyhelminths, or flatworms; the nematodes, or roundworms; and the acanthocephalans or spiny-headed worms. The platyhelminths and nematodes have free-living members but the acanthocephalans are entirely parasitic.

1.1 Platyhelminths (flatworms)

The three main groups of parasitic flatworms are the monogeneans, which are usually ectoparasites on fish, the digeneans, which are endoparasitic flukes, and the tapeworms.

1.1.1 Monogeneans

These usually occur on either the skin or gills of fish but some are endoparasites in the cloaca, oviducts or bladders of their hosts: for example, *Polystoma integerrimum* is a bladder parasite of frogs. Monogeneans are often highly host-specific; one species may be confined to one particular species of host. They have simple, direct life cycles (i.e. no intermediate host is involved). The hermaphrodite adult produces eggs which hatch into dispersive, ciliated oncomiracidia larvae which have hooked posterior attachment organs. These locate and infect the appropriate host fish and grow into adults with highly complex posterior attachment organs, as befits ectoparasites which are in a position to be easily dislodged from the host. An example of a common skin parasite is *Entobdella soleae* from the Dover sole, *Solea solea* (see Figs 1–1 and 3–2).

The creamy white adults, measuring 3–5 mm, can be removed from the underside of soles using a paintbrush or scalpel blade. If transferred to shallow glass dishes containing filtered sea-water and maintained at 10–15°C the adults lay tanned, tetrahedral eggs with long sticky filaments. Providing the sea-water is changed regularly, these hatch in just under four weeks at 14°C and the oncomiracidia swim around for 24 h during which time their specificity to sole scales relative to those from other fish can be investigated.

1.1.2 Digeneans

These largely endoparasitic flukes occur mostly in the vertebrate gut or its associated organs. The spiny adults can be recognized by their two suckers, typically an oral sucker surrounding the mouth and a ventral

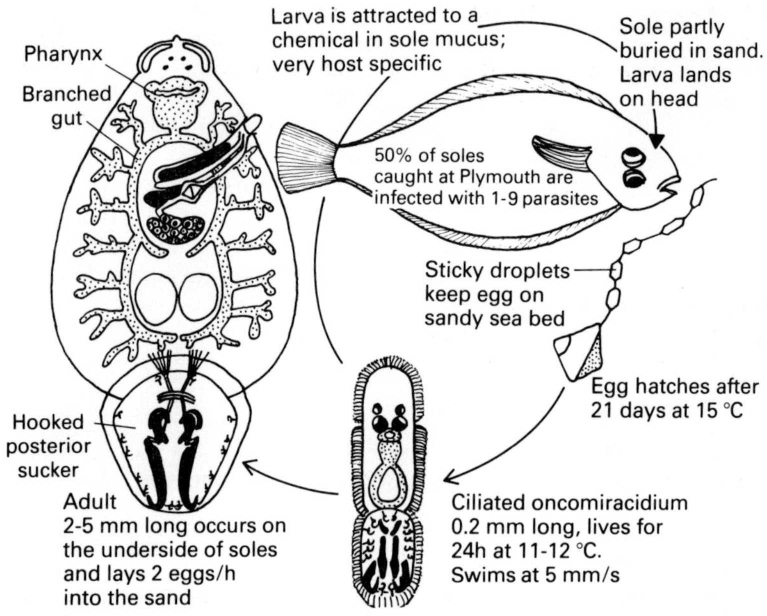

Fig. 1–1 Life cycle of the monogenean *Entobdella soleae*. (Details from KEARN, G. C. (1963). *Parasitology*, 53, 253–63.)

sucker or acetabulum. Digeneans have complex life cycles involving at least one intermediate host which is usually a snail. Asexual multiplication occurs whilst in this host to boost parasite numbers during the hazardous life cycle. This is so effective that one egg may ultimately produce up to one million cercariae. There are five main larval stages in the digenean life cycle: a ciliated miracidium, sporocyst, redia, cercaria and metacercaria. Daughter generations of sporocysts and redia may be produced and there are many variations on this plan in different flukes, for example a redial stage is absent from the life cycle of schistosome blood flukes. Dispersive miracidia penetrate into snails and shed their cilia to become active, muscular, brood sacs called sporocysts, which usually occur in the digestive glands of the snail and absorb nutrients over their body walls. Germ balls within the sporocysts develop into collared larvae with a gut, called rediae, and these in turn each produce numerous tailed cercaria larvae. The latter have an oral and ventral sucker resembling those of the adult and are dispersive, breaking out of the snail to infect either the second intermediate host (which may be either a vertebrate or invertebrate) or the final vertebrate host. Cercariae may do this either actively or passively. If the former, they are usually equipped with spines, stylets and penetration glands; if the latter, cercariae tend to encyst using cystogenous glands and are eaten by the host whilst protected within a cyst (the metacercarial stage). Some cercariae, however, penetrate the second intermediate host and then encyst within its tissues until eaten by the final host. In the final host the metacercaria excysts (see p. 42) and develops into an adult (Fig. 5–4). *Fasciola hepatica*, the liver fluke of sheep and cattle, is a digenean. It occurs mainly in the damp western parts of Britain in habitats suitable for survival of its amphibious snail host, *Lymnaea truncatula*. Another very important digenean genus is *Schistosoma*, different species of which live in the abdominal veins of man and cause schistosomiasis, or bilharzia, in tropical South America (*S. mansoni*), Africa (*S. mansoni*, *S. haematobium* and others) and the Far East (*S. japonicum*). This disease, which may affect 1000 million people, is actually increasing due to irrigation schemes which are encouraging the spread of digenean snail hosts (see pp. 57–58 and Fig. 1–2).

1.1.3 Cestodes (tapeworms)

These are also endoparasites, usually in the vertebrate gut. They lack a gut and feed via the body wall (p. 27). A tapeworm attaches using a small scolex which may bear hooks and suckers (Figs 3–4b and 3–5) and behind this is a neck followed by segments, or proglottids, which contain the hermaphrodite reproductive organs and become progressively more mature towards the end of the worm. In cyclophyllidean tapeworms that infect birds and mammals (e.g. *Taenia* and *Hymenolepis* spp.), the mature egg-containing proglottids drop off and are voided in the faeces.

Different groups of tapeworms infect different groups of vertebrate hosts. They have complex life cycles involving one or more intermediate hosts. The original intermediate host of primitive fish tapeworms was probably an aquatic arthropod but as the tapeworms adapted to infecting land vertebrates, these hosts were superseded firstly by terrestrial invertebrate hosts (snails, insects, mites, etc.) and eventually by vertebrate hosts. *Taenia solium* (the pork tapeworm of man) and *T. saginata* (the beef tapeworm) use the pig and cow respectively as intermediate hosts. The eggs of *T. solium* but not *T. saginata* can infect man and develop into cysticerci or bladder worms measuring up to 1.25 cm in diameter in tissues such as those of the muscles and nervous system. This condition (cysticercosis) is much more pathogenic than the effects of a single adult tapeworm in the intestine. The first larva hatching from the egg is an oncosphere with three pairs of hooks and this is usually non-ciliated in forms parasitizing land animals by which it is eaten inside the egg.

Once in the gut of the intermediate host the oncosphere hatches and bores out of the gut wall into the tissues where it encysts as either a cysticercoid larva (in hymenolepid tapeworms, see Fig. 1–3) or as a cysticercus or bladder worm (e.g. in taeniid tapeworms). These larvae excyst in the gut of the final host after being eaten so the life cycle is internalized, with no free-living stages, as an adaptation to terrestrial life cycles.

Another very important tapeworm is *Echinococcus granulosus* parasitic as

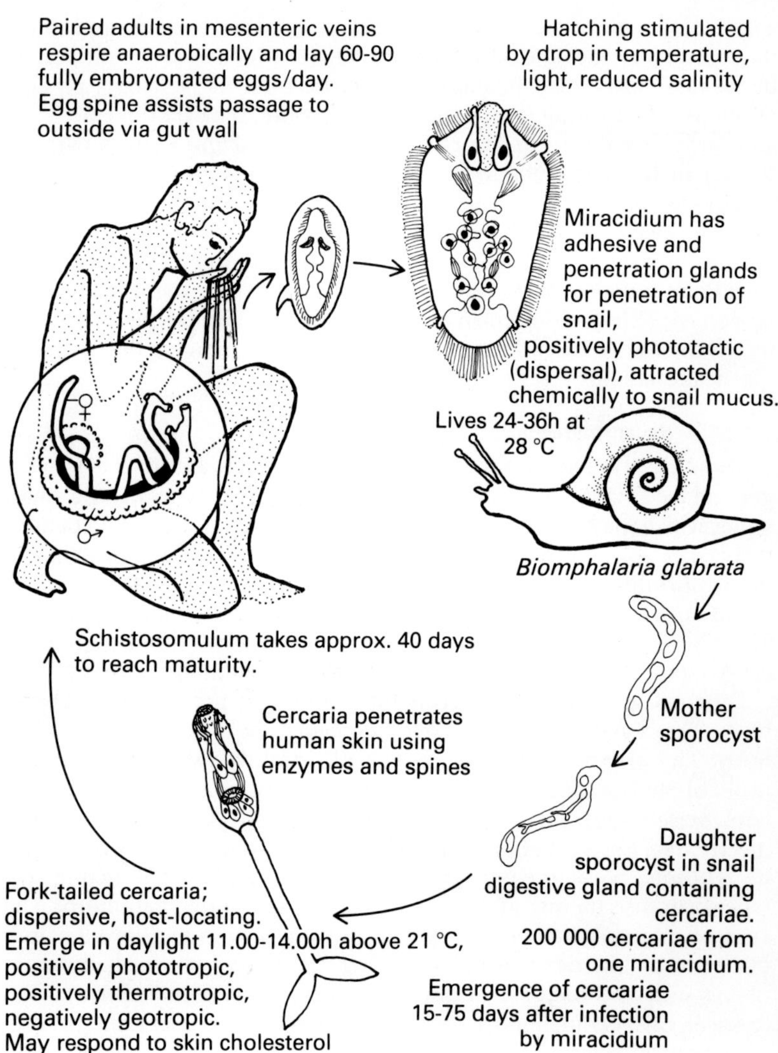

Fig. 1–2 Life cycle of the human blood fluke *Schistosoma mansoni*. (After various authors.)

an adult in the intestine of dog. It consists of only three proglottids but compensates by undergoing a massive asexual multiplication in the intermediate host which is usually a sheep but may be man or other mammal. Eggs can be picked up from the coat of dogs and when these are accidentally ingested the larvae locate in the tissues and develop into cysts, from the linings of which bud off millions of infective small scolices. Cysts

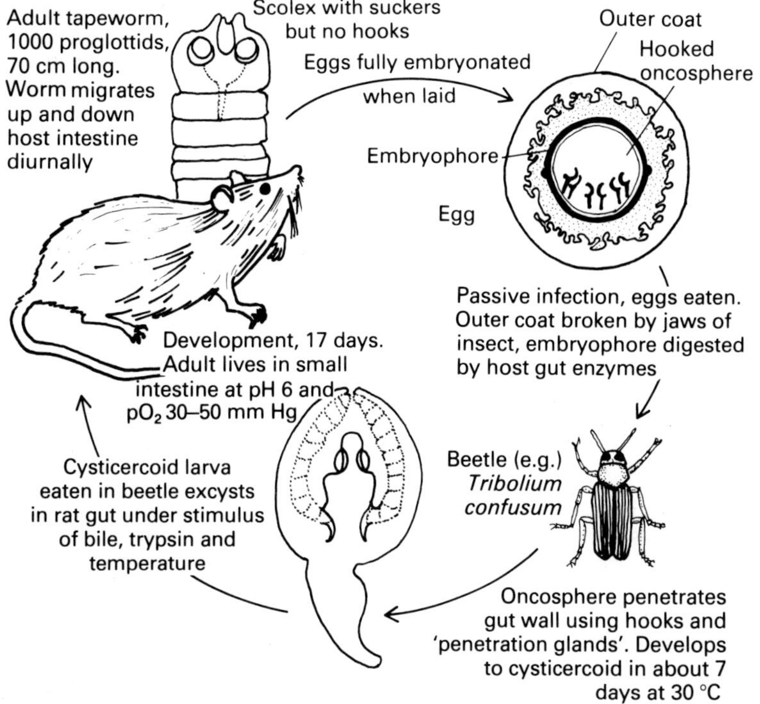

Fig. 1–3 Life cycle of the rat tapeworm *Hymenolepis diminuta*. (After various authors.)

are usually between 50–100 mm across but can grow to 500 mm (in cattle) and may contain daughter cysts and 12–18 litres of liquid. Cysts usually occur in the liver but sometimes invade the brain where the effects may be fatal.

1.2 Nematodes (roundworms)

Nematodes are cylindrical worms tapering at each end. The body is invested with a thick cuticle and unlike the platyhelminths, the gut has a mouth and anus. The sexes are usually separate and the males may be smaller than the females. They occur in various sites: some are internal or external parasites of plants, others are endoparasites in animal tissues. The life cycle involves an egg with a very resistant shell and various larval stages which moult to reach the adult stage. There are always four moults and the larval stages are called first, second, third and fourth stage larvae, or L_1–L_4 larvae. In the strongyle nematodes, a group including the hookworms and many important parasites of livestock, the L_3 larva is the infective stage that invades the final host. Some nematodes moult twice in the egg so that the larva hatches with two protective cuticles. In others the

L_2 cast cuticle is retained as a loose protective sheath around the L_3 larva. Intestinal parasites such as *Ascaris lumbricoides* (the roundworm of pig and man), *Haemonchus contortus* (the stomach worm of sheep, see Fig. 1–4), *Ancylostoma duodenale* and *Necator americanus* (the human hookworms) and *Enterobius vermicularis* (the human pinworm), all have direct life cycles and the hookworms have a skin-penetrating L_3 larva. *Wuchereria bancrofti* and other filarial nematodes causing elephantiasis are transmitted by mosquitoes which inject infective L_3 larvae into the bloodstream of man. From here the larvae invade the lymphatic system where the adults live.

Plant parasites have similar life cycles and infect the roots, stems, leaves and flowers of plants, often causing enormous economic losses. In addition to causing damage directly, they also do so by injecting plant viruses when they feed or by producing wounds that rapidly become infected by fungi and bacteria. Amongst the most serious of the plant parasitic nematodes are the potato root eel worm *Heterodera rostochiensis* and the stem and bulb parasite *Ditylenchus dipsaci*. In *Heterodera* L_2 larvae are liberated from cysts in the soil and invade the potato roots. These feed, moult and grow into adults. The male is slender and breaks out of the root first whereas the females are more swollen and break down the root until their bodies, still attached by the head, project into the soil. The motile males then fertilize the females which become converted to cyst-like structures. During the growing season the fertilized eggs develop as far as larvae in the females but in winter the cuticle of the female becomes hardened and although larvae develop within the eggs, they are not released until they receive an appropriate stimulus from the roots of the potato plant (p. 41).

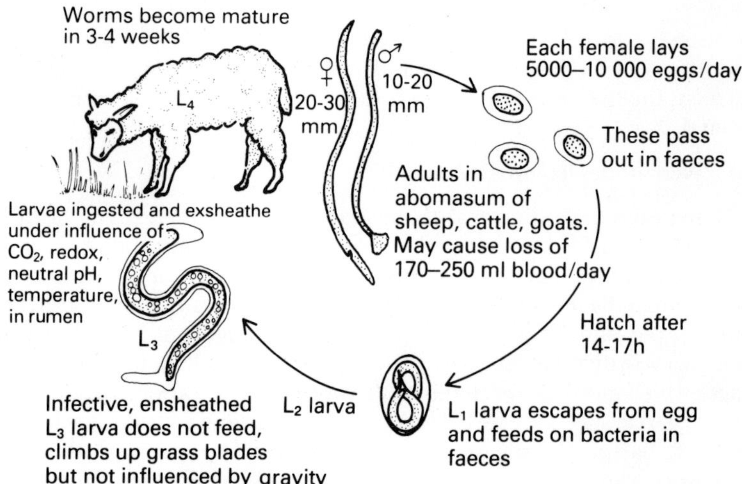

Fig. 1–4 Life cycle of the stomach worm of sheep *Haemonchus contortus* (Nematoda). (After various authors.)

1.3 Acanthocephalans (spiny-headed worms)

The most obvious feature of the adult is an invaginable proboscis armed with hooks. Adults range in size from 1.5 mm to over 500 mm but the majority are small. All lack a gut and feed across the body wall (p. 27); they are cylindrical in shape and have two sexes. They are endoparasites of vertebrates, largely in the gut of fish and birds. A typical life cycle is indirect and involves aquatic arthropods as intermediate hosts, but terrestrial forms have become adapted to land arthropods; for example, *Moniliformis dubius* in rats uses the cockroach *Periplaneta americana* as its intermediate host. A fairly common and widely spread species which has been much studied is *Polymorphus minutus* in the gut of wild fowl and domestic ducks. Eggs passing out in the faeces are eaten by the amphipod, *Gammarus* (see Fig. 1–5). The first larva is a spined acanthor which hatches from the egg in the gut and burrows into the haemocoel where it passes through an acanthella stage into an encysted stage called a cystacanth which is bright orange. Infected *Gammarus* are easily identified by a bright orange spot visible on the dorsal side. Infections of shrimps are usually low, between 1–4% in most localities, but may reach 30% in streams leading from duck ponds. When *Gammarus* is eaten by a duck the larva excysts (p. 42) and the proboscis evaginates and attaches to the intestine wall.

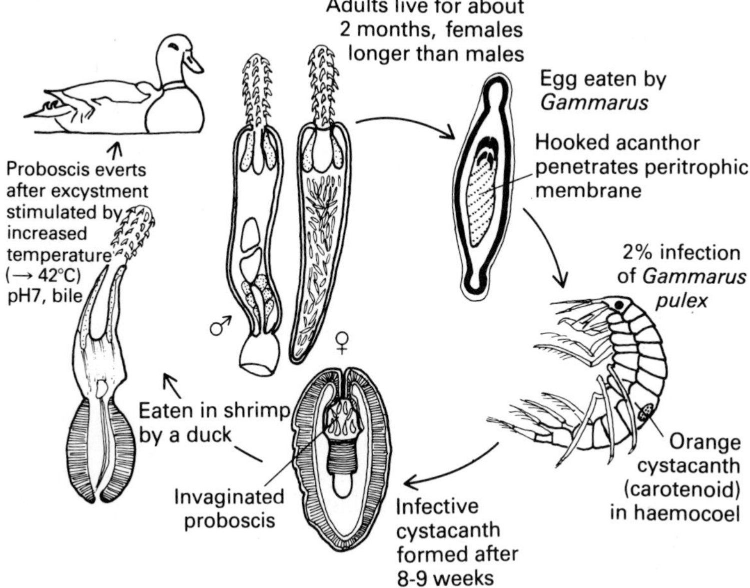

Fig. 1–5 Life cycle of *Polymorphus minutus* (Acanthocephala). (After various authors.)

2 The Parasitic Way of Life – Advantages and Problems

2.1 Advantages of parasitism and evolutionary commitment

An organism that can successfully establish itself outside or inside another living organism has much to gain from its host, for it is provided (particularly in the case of tissue parasites) with a regulated environment and a supply of food and other metabolites. A parasitic way of life has evolved on many separate occasions and most major groups of animals have parasitic members. The platyhelminth and nematode groups have both free-living and parasitic members and parasitism probably evolved at least twice in the platyhelminths (in the monogenean-cestode and digenean lines) and several times in the nematodes. The acanthocephalans are all parasitic and the type of free-living ancestor from which this group arose is not known.

Given the obvious advantages offered by the parasitic way of life it is all too easy to ignore the problems that a parasitic existence involves. These problems exist at three main levels. Firstly there are problems of *maintenance* in the intermediate and final hosts, often against the host's defence reactions. Secondly there are problems in *transmission* from host to host, and thirdly there are special problems at an *evolutionary level* caused by the fact that the environment of parasites comprises other living and evolving organisms which interact with the parasite. This means the parasite has, over many generations, to keep pace with the evolutionary progress of the host or hosts.

2.1.1 *Specialization and commitment*

In many instances the evolution of a parasite and its host or hosts may be closely linked so that the parasite evolves in parallel with the host. Parasites that have been associated for long periods of their evolutionary history with a particular group of hosts may have evolved so closely with them that as the hosts speciate so do the parasites, so that each host species tends to have its own species of parasites. This produces physiological host-specificity with the parasite becoming increasingly closely adapted to living in a particular site in or on a particular species of host or group of related hosts and progressively less able to adapt to conditions in other host species. Even if attempts are made experimentally to infect foreign hosts with a highly host-specific parasite, they will fail either because the parasite cannot establish itself in the foreign host or because, for instance, some metabolite necessary for growth and reproduction is absent.

Not all helminths become specific to their final vertebrate hosts.

Digenean flukes are highly specific to their mollusc intermediate hosts but far less so to their final vertebrate hosts. This is probably because they were originally parasites of snails and have been associated with them for longer than vertebrates. The liver fluke, *Fasciola hepatica*, is fairly specific to the mud snail *Lymnaea truncatula* (although this specificity is not absolute and development can be induced experimentally in immature related snails such as *L. stagnalis*, *L. palustris*, *L. glabra* and *L. pereger*) but has been found to occur naturally in a wide range of herbivorous and omnivorous vertebrates – sheep, horses, cattle, pigs, goats, donkeys and man. This kind of relationship results from the parasite being picked up as an infective cyst from grass and other vegetation such as watercress, so that hosts that share the same diet can become infected with the fluke which is competent to develop in a wide range of vertebrate hosts. This looser kind of specificity is called *ecological specificity* because the pattern of distribution of the parasite depends upon the shared ecology or feeding habits of the various (genetically unrelated) hosts. So *Fasciola* shows strict physiological specificity to its snail intermediate host but a looser ecological specificity to its final vertebrate host.

Physiological specificity is advantageous in that it produces close adaptation between parasite and host but does demand increasing specialization in both a morphological and physiological sense and restriction of the host range.

2.1.2 *Loss and gain by parasites*

Parasites become highly modified in relation to their way of life and tend to lose structures such as eyespots, locomotory organelles (cilia) or even the gut, as has occurred independently in cestodes, acanthocephalans and the larval parasitic nematode, *Mermis*. The behaviour patterns and metabolic pathways of parasites may also be simplified. Because parasites may appear simple compared with free-living members of the same group, they are often termed 'degenerate'. In fact parasites are highly specialized to their way of life and do *develop* morphological and physiological specializations as well as lose them. The often extremely complex attachment organs of parasites such as the monogenean gill flukes are an obvious example.

In addition, although the adult stage may be simplified in some respects, the larvae of the same parasite may retain many features characteristic of independent life. Many miracidium larvae of flukes have cilia and eyespots, for example.

When it is considered that a digenean parasite may have six or more different stages in its life history, some free-living and dispersive, others parasitic in perhaps as many as three different hosts, then it can be appreciated that, far from being simplified this parasite has elaborated rather than reduced its genetic programme, the different characters being expressed in relation to the appropriate environment at different times in the life history. A parasite is not just its adult stage but all the stages in its entire life history which together must be adapted to withstand vast shifts in ecology from ectothermic to endothermic hosts and perhaps to periods of free-living existence.

2.2 The problems of maintenance in the host and transmission between hosts

2.2.1 *Site location*

Since most parasites are site-specific as well as host-specific, the infective stages in order to survive have to be able to locate a particular organ or tissue in or on the host. The parasite must be able to interpret chemical and other clues that allow it to home in on the appropriate site for establishment. Site selection is not a problem unique to parasitism for it is also important to many sessile marine invertebrates such as barnacles and oysters.

2.2.2 *Survival and feeding*

Once *in situ* the parasite has to be able to resist host defence reactions whether tissue reactions such as encapsulation and digestion, or specific humoral, antibody reactions. Blood parasites are particularly exposed to these humoral immune reactions and have ingenious methods of resisting them. Invading gut parasites must be able to resist the host's digestive enzymes and juices including hydrochloric acid and surfactants such as bile. A parasite also has to attach securely, especially if in a duct or blood vessel where dislodgement is likely, and it has to be able to feed without damaging host tissues so much as to elicit an immune response, or to cause death of the host.

2.2.3 *Respiration and excretion*

Gut parasites, unless near the mucosa, tend to live in low oxygen tensions and may have to respire anaerobically (but see p. 32). Again this is not special to parasites but occurs in other animals living in oxygen deficient conditions such as marine and fresh-water muds, or waters warmed either naturally or by thermal pollution. The anaerobic respiration of parasites results in the excretion of incompletely metabolized fatty acids and in some cases alcohols. These and other excretory products must not be excessively toxic to the host, for by curtailing the host's reproductive efficiency or causing its death, the parasite is damaging its own livelihood.

2.2.4 *Competition*

The parasite may have to compete, not only with the host, for the food and metabolites it needs, but also with other members of its own species and with other species of parasite that may compete for the same site.

2.2.5 *Reproduction*

Cross-fertilization is the rule in nearly all parasites, even hermaphrodites, so the parasite has to be able to find a mate in the host at the same stage of reproductive maturity as itself. The reproductive rate of parasites also has to be high since, particularly in parasites with complex life histories, the chances of locating the various intermediate and final hosts may be low and sufficient offspring have to be produced to counteract the inevitable losses. Many free-living animals (e.g. the herring) also produce large numbers of eggs to counteract losses due to factors such as external fertilization and predation, so this is not a feature of the parasitic mode of life only. Reproductive output is not simply a matter of numbers of eggs or larvae produced by sexual and asexual reproduction; the generation time (i.e. the time taken to produce the next reproductive stage, for instance an egg-laying female) is also important. An organism that produces few eggs but has a rapid generation time may have a higher reproductive output or biotic potential than one that produces millions of eggs that take many months to become sexually mature. The generation time also determines the rate at which new mutations can be spread through the population and a fast generation time may lead to evolutionary plasticity. Despite their specialization, parasites maintain a high capacity for adaptation, as is shown by production of new drug-resistant strains and strains adapted to new host types.

Although parasites may need to produce large numbers of offspring they must match their population dynamics with those of the host in order not to saturate, and risk damaging, too high a proportion of the host population. Parasites may therefore be involved with population regulation as well as fecundity.

2.2.6 *Transmission*

Parasites must be able to get their eggs and larvae out of their host and this may present a considerable problem for tissue parasites which may have to depend on vectors, such as biting flies. Once outside the host the parasite must be able to survive, perhaps for long periods, and may have protective structures such as cysts, egg shells or cuticles. The intermediate stages may have to remain dormant until specific stimuli activate them either to disperse the parasite or bring it into the host environment. Infective stages whether invading the host actively (e.g. by boring through the skin) or passively (e.g. by being swallowed) still must be able to recognize the correct host. Active penetration into the host may involve spines, stylets or digestive enzymes.

2.2.7 *Dispersal in space and time*

Parasites have to disperse themselves actively or passively amongst their host populations in time as well as in space. This is important when a parasite can infect its host, or perhaps particular stages of its host, only at certain times of year, and has to synchronize its own life cycle with that of the host.

2.2.8 *Plant parasites*

Plant parasites share many of the same problems as animal parasites, but in addition have specific problems associated with penetrating the cellulose cell walls of their hosts. This may involve the use of stylets or cellulase enzymes.

2.3 What makes a successful parasite?

A successful parasite is one that is in balance with its host. Only a poorly-adapted parasite exploits its relationship with its host to the extent of reducing the host's reproductive capacity or killing the host (at least before it has reproduced). The parasite therefore has to be carefully attuned to the biology of the host and, because it is partner to a living system, has to be sufficiently flexible, in an evolutionary sense, to be able to evolve in phase with the host. It should profit from new evolutionary opportunities and yet resist the superior host defence mechanisms that develop as the host's evolutionary experience of the parasite accumulates. The host and parasite are really interdependent, and it has been suggested that even the antagonistic reactions of one upon the other may be beneficial. Disease could be a useful curb on the host population whilst the immune reaction could act as a natural brake on parasite numbers and prevent them building up to lethal levels.

Unfortunately our ideas about parasite pathogenicity are conditioned by our experience of the parasites of man and domestic animals. Some of these parasites tend to kill their hosts and this may be because the parasite is 'new' in an evolutionary sense and may not have had enough time to adapt to man. This is thought to be the case for trypanosome protozoans causing sleeping sickness. Trypanosomes are really parasites of wild game in which they cause little apparent harm; it is only when in unnatural hosts such as man or domestic cattle that they cause death. On the other hand, parasites that have evolved in man such as the hookworms may build up to unnatural levels in the artificially crowded societies man creates and cause harm because of the abnormally high parasite burdens carried.

3 Attachment and Maintenance in the Host

3.1 Attachment

The larval stages of many parasites are specially adapted for attaching to their hosts during the course of penetration, which usually occurs directly through the skin or, after being swallowed, across the gut lining. The ciliated miracidium larva of digeneans attaches to the exposed skin surface of snails using its probe-like apical papillum which is glandular and thought to secrete both adhesive mucus and digestive enzymes to assist penetration. The tip of this papillum can be depressed to form a temporary sucker. Miracidia of *Fasciola hepatica* shed their covering of ciliated cells during penetration but schistosome larvae retain them. The body wall of the miracidium is very muscular and wriggling movements assist penetration. Schistosome cercariae use a similar method of attack. They first attach with the ventral sucker, often in a groove in the skin surface. Having gained a foothold they then attach with the oral sucker through which various secretions are poured. One secretion is a hydrating mucus that imbibes water and swells, pushing up skin scales under which the cercariae wriggle (Fig. 3–1). Hyaluronidase and collagenase enzymes are also discharged from another set of glands. Small spines on the anterior surface of the body assist penetration and this sometimes occurs through hair follicles. Other types of cercariae have spiny collars (e.g. echinostomes) (Fig. 3–4a) or stylets (xiphidiocercariae) to aid penetration. The tail of the cercaria is shed during penetration.

In contrast, the ensheathed L_3 larvae of the cat hookworm *Ancylostoma tubaeforme* do not seem to use enzymes but rely largely on mechanical means of penetration, although possibly alkaline secretions that dissociate skin cells may be involved. Non-enzymatic penetration may be true of other hookworms too.

Larval helminths that penetrate through the gut after being swallowed may have spines or hooks to assist them. The newly-excysted juvenile of the liver fluke is shown in Fig. 5–4. It doubtless uses its body spines in boring through the gut wall and in penetrating the liver capsule. Tapeworm oncosphere larvae have six hooks and may be assisted by secretions from the so-called penetration glands in boring through the gut of their intermediate hosts before encysting in muscles.

With regard to adult helminths, secure attachment is particularly important in monogenean ectoparasites which have to resist being pulled off the body of their fish hosts by water currents. Their basic adhesive equipment consists of a posterior sucker which is usually armed with hard

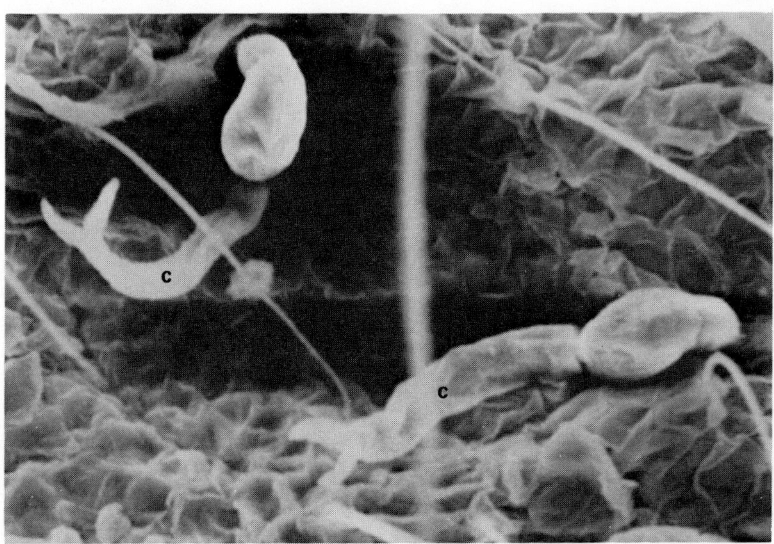

Fig. 3–1 Scanning electron micrograph of *Schistosoma mansoni* cercariae (c) exploring mouse ear skin. Note flattened, keratinized epidermal cells and hairs. × 100. (From STIRLWALT, M. A. and DORSEY, C. H. (1974). *Exp. Parasit.*, 35, 1–15.)

spines, hooks or clamps and anterior adhesive glands which secrete a kind of underwater glue. These adhesive organs are beautifully designed to fit the appropriate attachment site either on the skin or the gills of the host. Skin parasites tend to have large flat suckers which may be subdivided into further sucking cups. There is often a flange around the edge as a seal and a number of peripheral hooklets. Large hooks called hamuli are associated with the centre of the sucker and in *Entobdella soleae* one pair act as props to lift up the roof of the sucker and cause the initial suction whilst the longest pair support the roof of the sucker and also anchor into the host's skin. Scanning electron micrographs show the under surface of the sucker of *E. soleae* to be covered with a series of 'bumps'; these were at first thought to form a non-slip surface, but in fact contain nerve endings and may be sense organs, perhaps proprioceptors coordinating sucker action (Fig. 3–2). The dorso-ventral muscles of this sucker appear to contain paramyosin filaments (an especially thick form of myosin). This could possibly be associated with a catch mechanism locking attachment muscles in a contracted state so that little energy would be required for the parasite to hang on.

LLEWELLYN (1956) has shown that in gill parasitic forms the hooklets and hamuli are typically confined to a small posterior lappet and the main attachment organ is developed from a new region anterior to this. This

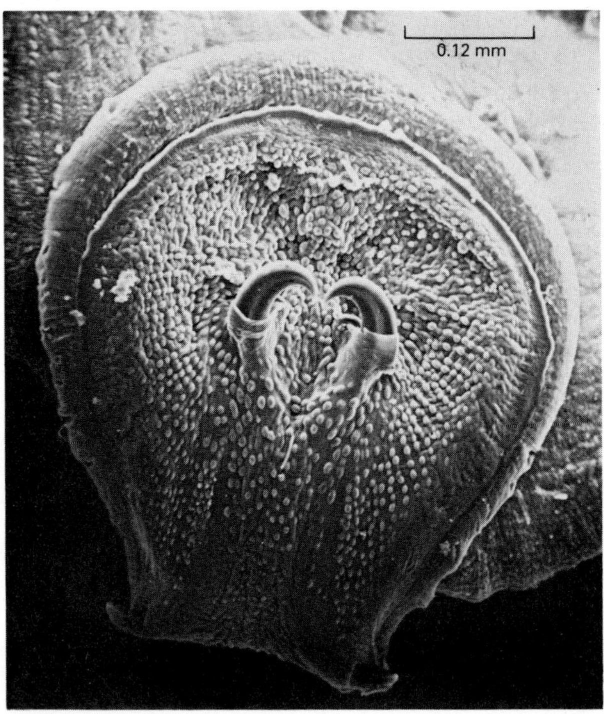

Fig. 3–2 Scanning electron micrograph of the posterior sucker of *Entobdella soleae* showing hooks and sensory 'bumps'. ×640. (From LYONS, K. M. (1973). *Z. Zellforsch.*, **137**, 471–80.)

organ is subdivided into rows of modified suckers on each side of the body which are usually supported by a framework of hard sclerites forming a device that can be clamped onto the gills of a fish (Fig. 3–3). The clamps usually attach to the secondary gill lamellae and the size of the clamp corresponds to the size of the attachment site in a particular species of host. Each parasite has a specific adhesive attitude on the gills and is aligned with the gill ventilating current so as to be maximally streamlined. The adhesive organs are upstream and the head trails in the water current. Some highly modified gill parasites have become asymmetrical and have lost the adhesive organs on one side to conform to the asymmetrical direction of the gill ventilating current (Fig. 3–3). Some species show a marked predilection for a particular gill. Thus *Diclidophora merlangi* occurs more frequently on the first gill of whiting, *D. luscae* on the second and third gill of pout. Occasionally a fish is parasitized with two kinds of mongenean gill fluke in which case each has its own particular

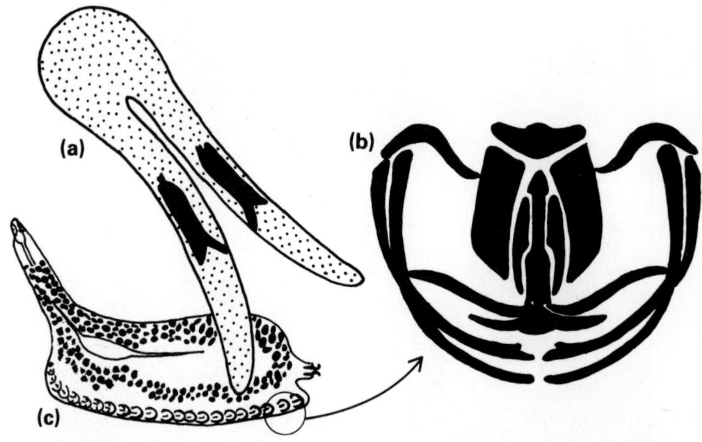

Fig. 3–3 Diagram of (a) right and left 'footed' *Gastrocotyle trachuri* (Monogenea) adapted to live on inner and outer hemibranchs of the horse mackerel (from LLEWELLYN, J. (1957). *Host specificity in monogenetic trematodes.* In: First Symposium on Host Specificity among Parasites of Vertebrates. Neuchâtel. University of Neuchâtel, 199–211); (b) detail of the hard framework of a single clamp of *Gastrocotyle*; (c) diagram of adult *Gastrocotyle*.

site; for example, *Gastrocotyle trachuri* occurs on the sides, *Pseudaxine trachuri* on the tips, of the primary gill lamellae of horse mackerel.

The preferred site for the attachment of vertebrate gut parasites is probably the first part of the small intestine which is not only rich in digested food but may also be less affected by muscular activity. Even so, peristalsis occurs here and it has been shown that villi relax and contract some six times a minute.

Adult digenean flukes are usually flat and therefore streamlined and use an oral and blind ventral sucker for attachment. The oral sucker may be associated with adhesive glands and both may be spined. Backwardly pointing body spines may also aid attachment. Tapeworms attach by means of an apical scolex which may be disproportionately small. The type of scolex varies according to the group (see Figs 3–4b and 3–5). In tetraphyllidean parasites of skates and rays the patterns on the suckers may match the patterns of crypts and villi in specific sites on the wall of the spiral valve. CARVAJAL and DAILEY (1975) have shown that at least three species of tetraphyllid may occur in the spiral valve of a single skate, each with its own attachment site. In addition to the scolex hooks and suckers, the whole surface of tapeworms is covered with microscopic body spines with recurved tips called microtriches (Figs 4–1 and 4–2). These are similar in size to the microvilli of the host's gut cells and could play an important part in attachment.

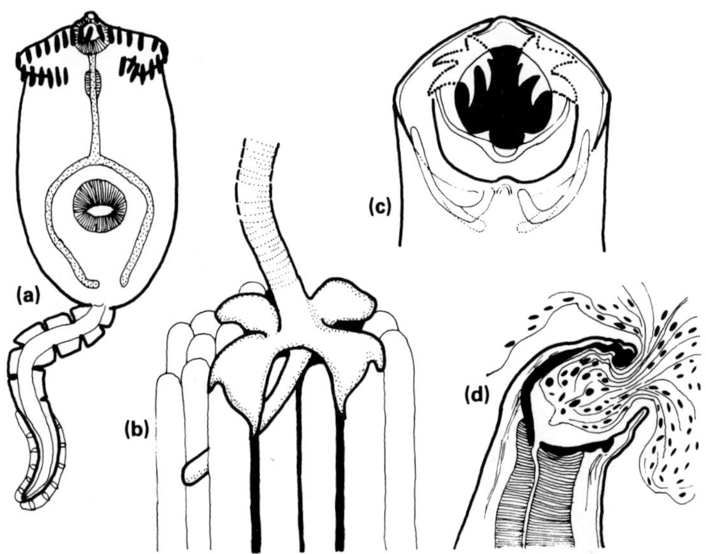

Fig. 3–4 Various attachment organs: (**a**) echinostome cercaria; (**b**) scolex of tetraphyllidean tapeworm (*Pseudanthobothrium*) from rays. (After H. H. Williams from BAER, J. G. (1971). *Animal Parasites*, Weidenfeld and Nicolson, London.) (**c**) human hookworm *Ancylostoma duodenale* showing cutting mouthparts; (**d**) section through the head of *Ancylostoma* showing attachment to the gut wall.

Acanthocephalans have a spiny, protrusible proboscis armed with recurved hooks which is operated by a special closed fluid pressure system separated from the main body region. When the tip of the proboscis is invaginated the hooks neatly lift off the gut wall.

Nematodes attach mainly using the buccal cavity which may be armed with cutting plates, spines or stylets (Fig. 3–4c). Suction pressure is created by the pharynx. Many sensory papillae are situated around the lips and a pair of amphids each side of the head contain sensory endings.

3.2 Maintenance in the host gut

Gut parasites have to resist the effects of acid, bile and host enzymes. Platyhelminths, which all have a living cytoplasmic tegument, probably do this in a similar way to the host gut surface itself, which relies on protective mucous coverings, resistant plasma membrane composition and tight junctions between the cells. Tapeworms and flukes are covered with a surface coat of mucopolysaccharide or mucoprotein which is closely bound into the surface plasma membrane. This is rich in sialic acid

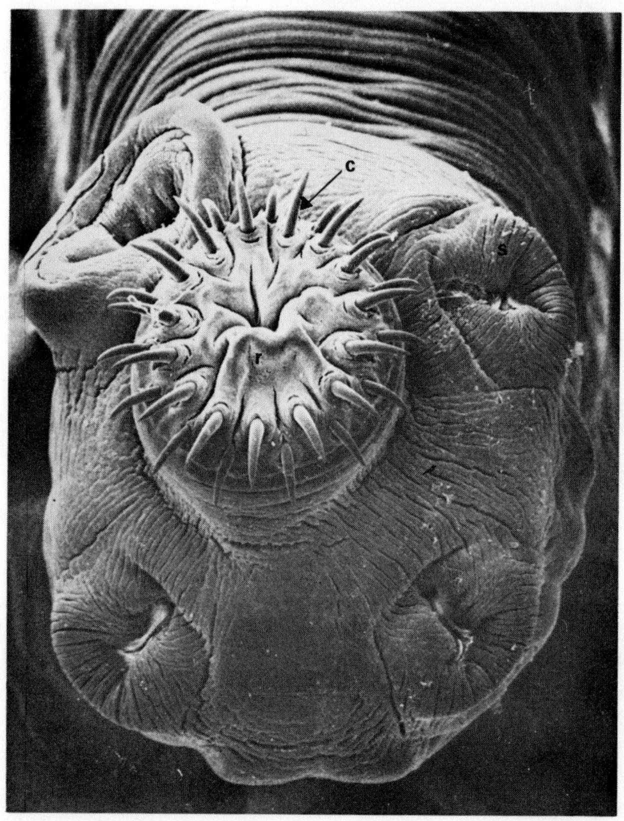

Fig. 3–5 Scanning electron micrograph of the adult scolex of *Taenia hydatigena* showing **c** – circlet of staggered hooks; **r** – rostellum; **s** – suckers. × 170. (From FEATHERSTON, D. W. (1975). *Int. J. Parasit.*, 5, 615–19.)

groups which somehow makes it highly resistant to digestion. Work using labelled sugars that become incorporated into the surface coat and are 'tracked' using autoradiography at electron microscope level, showed that in the rat tapeworm, *Hymenolepis diminuta*, the surface coat has a fast turnover and is renewed every six to eight hours. Mucus is also copiously secreted from the tegument. It is not known how rapidly the tegument itself breaks down and regenerates; cell renewal in the lining of the vertebrate gut is very rapid. There has long been an idea that tapeworms may produce enzyme-inhibitors, but this has not been established definitely. Gut parasites might, however, inactivate host enzymes by manipulating the pH and the rat tapeworm is known to acidify the small intestine *in vivo* by absorbing bicarbonate and secreting H^+ ions. Similar exchange mechanisms which regulate the worm's tissue pH might explain how digeneans, such as *Derogenes*, a hemiurid fluke, manage to survive in the stomach of marine fish. The protective action of mucus and the syncytial nature of fluke (and tapeworm) teguments with few, if any, boundaries for penetration of acid and enzymes, may also be important. Nematode worms are covered by a toughened cuticle which is protective although still permeable to water, certain ions and very small molecules so that the main regulatory surface is at the level of the living hypodermis underlying the cuticle.

Helminths may have surface membrane lipids that are resistant to the effects of bile. Although bile may provide a specific trigger to hatching or excystment, it must be a difficult feature of the environment of adult worms. Different vertebrate groups may have different bile compositions and the reaction of the parasite to bile may play a part in determining host specificity. Carnivore bile, for example, is rich in salts of cholic acid whereas herbivore bile contains high levels of salts of deoxycholic acid. The dog tapeworm, *Echinococcus granulosus*, is rapidly lysed by sodium deoxycholate but is unaffected by cholate so is apparently not equipped to survive as an adult in a herbivore host.

3.3 Evading the host's immune reactions

A host may discourage establishment of a helminth parasite in several ways. If the parasite is unable to become established from the start the host is said to show *innate* or *natural immunity* to the parasite and there may be a genetic basis to this. If an initial infection induces a degree of resistance to subsequent infections, this is termed *acquired immunity*. The immune reaction is caused by recognition of some part of the parasite or of secretions or excretory products it produces. The time at which a parasite is most likely to alert host immune reactions is in tissue-living or migrating phases when it comes into maximum contact with cells of the surveillance system. Nevertheless, even gut parasites which might be thought to be largely outside the immune defence system can elicit a host reaction and may be spontaneously eliminated by a so-called 'self-cure' reaction.

3.3.1 The self-cure reaction

The best studied model is provided by *Nippostrongylus brasiliensis* in rats. When rats are heavily infected with L_3 skin penetrating larvae, eggs first appear in the faeces on the sixth day, peak egg production occurs on the tenth and then falls to zero in the following week (Fig. 3–6). This is accompanied by a massive expulsion of worms from the gut. A few remain but these are mostly males or, if female, sterile. When only a light infection is given worm expulsion is more gradual and if very small continuous infections are given, fertile worms can persist for more than three months in the gut and somehow become adapted to the immune

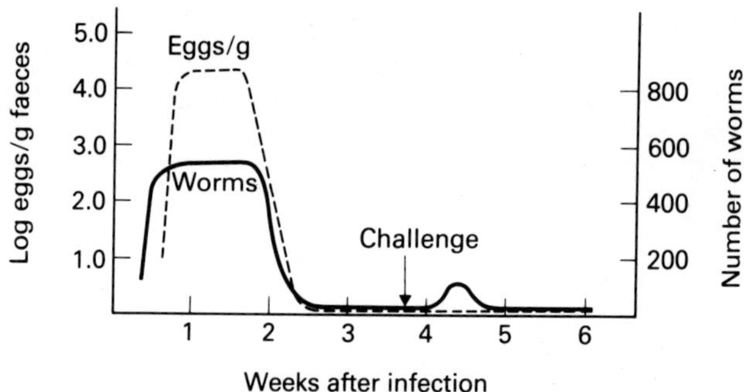

Fig. 3–6 The self-cure reaction to *Nippostrongylus brasiliensis* in rats. Peak egg production occurs on the 10th day of infection but after this an immune response eliminates most of the worms leaving a low level of infection. A subsequent challenge infection fails to become established for long. (By permission of Dr R. F. Phillipson in SMYTH, J. D. (1976). *Introduction to Animal Parasitology*, 2nd edn, Hodder and Stoughton, London and Sydney.)

response because if transferred to an immune host they survive to produce viable eggs. Although light infections may be a more natural occurrence, the parasite can be said to be adapted to the self-cure reaction elicited by heavy infections by developing rapidly to maturity and producing many eggs before expulsion from the host occurs. Rats which have thrown off a primary infection are very resistant to challenge infections. This type of resistance does not develop until the rats are five weeks old so that young animals are much more susceptible to infection. The precise cause of the self-cure reaction is not known, indeed it varies in different types of infection. It may be stimulated by the parasite penetrating too far into the mucosa or perhaps by mucoantigens at the gut surface and it may involve cell infiltration and production of various classes of antibody, including immunoglobulin E which is thought to be associated with histamine release causing an allergic type of response. The precise effect of antibodies on the worms is not known but they appear to affect the gut and prevent normal feeding. Reabsorption of sperm occurs and egg production ceases. Self-cure reactions are known for other gut parasitic nematodes and its consequence on the population dynamics of *Haemonchus contortus*, a parasite of sheep, is discussed on p. 49. Possibly this type of rejection helps the parasite not to overexploit the host in heavy infections and acts as a natural population regulator.

3.3.2 Immunologically privileged sites

Some sites in hosts show less reaction to parasites and foreign material introduced experimentally than others. These include the urinary tract, cornea and central nervous system and they are called immunologically privileged sites because the parasites occupying them may be relatively safe from host attack. On the other hand, parasites living in lymph and blood must be very vulnerable and the latter seem to have evolved special avoidance mechanisms.

3.3.3 Schistosome immunity – molecular mimicry

Adult schistosomes are capable of surviving for many years in the blood of their hosts, a remarkably immunologically hostile medium. Evidence is accumulating to suggest that adult schistosomes evade the immune response of their hosts by coating themselves with host antigens that serve as a mask concealing the parasite. As reviewed by CLEGG (1972) the bound host antigens have been shown, using immunological methods, to be likely to be glycolipids similar to those on host red blood cells acquired from the plasma, and schistosomula larvae cultured separately *in vitro* with host blood of different groups have been shown to bind antigens of the same blood group as the incubating medium. The location of the host antigens has been studied with an electron microscope using ferritin-labelled antibodies which attach to bound antigen, thus acting as an electron dense marker. The marker becomes associated with the outside membranes of the worm's tegument, suggesting that the antigen is bound superficially. Transplantation experiments also suggest that schistosomes adopt the identity of the hosts in which they have matured and if adult schistosomes grown in a mouse are transferred to a monkey previously immunized against mouse red cells, most of the 'mouse' schistosomes are destroyed. Worms grown in mice and transferred to the portal system of normal monkeys, however, survive well. The destruction process that occurs in the immune host has been studied with an electron microscope and the first signs of damage occur in the tegument which becomes vacuolated and then breaks down. Only when breakdown occurs do host phagocytic cells become involved.

Although the results reviewed provide one explanation of the *molecular mimicry* between parasite and host, there are other theories that seek to explain this in different ways (Fig. 3–7). One theory proposes that parasites come to resemble their hosts antigenically by convergence and natural selection, another suggests that during infection the host somehow induces the parasite to produce host-like antigens. The first idea seems to be incompatible with results of the schistosome transplantation experiments and with the finding that these parasites apparently bind host antigens; however, there could be a basis of truth in it which might apply better to other host-parasite situations. The second theory must also remain open until it is shown exactly where the antigenic disguise originates since it is still possible that the parasite could synthesize its own disguise in response to models provided by host antigens.

A peculiarity of the schistosome's ability to evade the host's immune

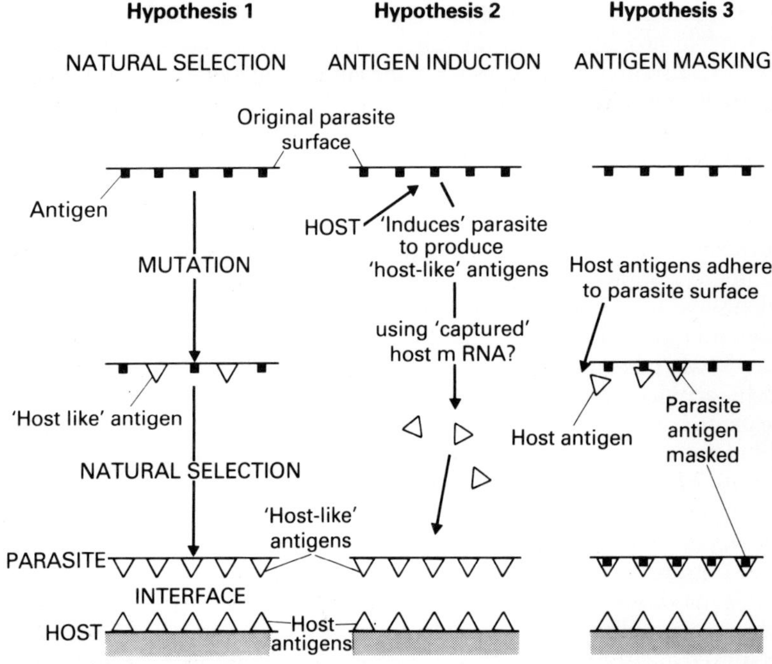

Fig. 3–7 'Molecular mimicry' in parasites; three possible hypotheses to explain the apparent occurrence of host or host-like antigens on parasite surfaces. (From SMYTH, J. D. (1973). Some interface phenomena in parasitic protozoa and helminths. Reproduced by permission of the National Research Council of Canada from *Canad. J. Zool.*, **51**, 367–77.)

response is that whilst established worms escape this, invading worms do elicit a host response and are eliminated. This type of immunity is termed concomitant immunity and, strangely, experiments reviewed by SMITHERS and TERRY (1976) suggest that it is the living *adult* worm that provides the major stimulus for this type of acquired immunity and not the invasive stages. Antibodies against both adult and larval schistosomes can, however, be detected in the serum of infected animals and tests for them can be used to diagnose early infections. The disease of schistosomiasis is largely caused by pathological reactions to the eggs of the parasite which have to work their way through the walls of the blood vessels and bladder or gut so as to find their way out of the host in faeces or urine. The eggs trigger off cell-mediated immunity and may eventually become surrounded by dense granuloma tissue.

3.4 Cross-immunity

Immunity is usually specific and typically involves the host being alerted to one particular species of parasite; however, cross-immunity has recently been found to exist. This means that an infection with one parasite may 'accidentally' confer resistance, sometimes to a completely unrelated parasite. For example, infecting a mouse with L_3 larvae of the dog hookworm *Ancylostoma caninum* increases resistance to subsequent infections with another nematode, *Trichinella spiralis*. In this case the immunity is reversible and primary infections with *T. spiralis* would protect against subsequent challenge with *A. caninum*. Cross-immunity is not always reversible. A possible explanation for the phenomenon is that these invasive larvae both use the same type of penetrating enzymes that elicit a similar host response.

3.5 Vaccines

The ability of a host to mount an immune reaction to its parasites has stimulated research to produce an effective vaccine and irradiated L_3 larvae of *Haemonchus contortus* (the stomach worm of sheep), *Dictyocaulus viviparus* (lung worm of cattle) and irradiated metacercariae of *F. hepatica* have been used as vaccines with varying degrees of success. The commercial vaccine produced against parasitic bronchitis has been most successful but the vaccine against *H. contortus* and *F. hepatica* less so. Unfortunately no effective vaccine has been found against *Schistosoma* spp. because although normal living cercariae are immunogenic, irradiated (and harmless) cercariae are not nearly as effective.

3.6 Parasite destruction by the immune response

There are two main kinds of immune response in vertebrates: a humoral response that depends on circulating antibody, and a cell-mediated response that involves recognition of fixed antigen by antibody-carrying cells. The latter is mainly concerned with the so-called allergic reactions or delayed hypersensitivity. In the humoral response, antibodies destroy invading organisms in various ways: by agglutination, i.e. sticking the surfaces of organisms together, and by lysis, i.e. punching holes in surface membranes bearing antigen to which antibody becomes bound. This reaction may involve a serum factor called complement. Complement may also be involved in phagocytosis where phagocytic cells attach to and destroy the invader. The immune response probably acts largely on the membrane surfaces of platyhelminth parasites, as described for schistosomes in an incompatible host, but as nematodes have a thick resistant cuticle, damage probably affects the gut cell surfaces and precipitation reactions may also occur at body pores which may block normal functioning. Some parasites capitalize on the host reaction and turn it to advantage; the liver fluke is thought to browse on the rapidly regenerating lining of the bile ducts that irritation with its body spines has produced.

3.7 Resistance mechanisms in invertebrates

The chief reactions of invertebrates to foreign material are to phagocytose it or to surround it with a capsule so cutting off the supply of metabolites. Some parasites counter the latter reaction by secreting a cyst which protects them. The acanthocephalan *Moniliformis dubius* lives in the haemocoel of a cockroach intermediate host and as an acanthor larva evades the host haemocytic response by secreting a non-cellular envelope around itself. Removal of the envelope leads to encapsulation. Similar types of phagocytic response have been described in molluscs. Such responses may be specific and can be enhanced by a previous infection. Factors that initiate phagocytosis are not known. As yet substances similar to antibodies have not yet been demonstrated in invertebrate body fluids.

3.8 Resistance to plant parasitic nematodes

Plants are by no means as passive to exploitation by animals as has been imagined and they have often powerful resistance mechanisms to parasite invasion. These are not yet completely understood but there is evidence that substances termed agglutinins, in some ways analogous to antibodies, are produced that damage invaders. These and other resistance mechanisms have been reviewed by WEBSTER (1975) and involve isolating, starving and poisoning invading larvae. Some crucifers are naturally resistant to the potato root eelworm, *Heterodera rostochiensis*, because they secrete mustard oils which kill motile larvae. Similarly french marigolds (*Tagetes* sp.) secrete polythienyls which suppress development of many types of plant nematodes. Chemical effects of this type between members of different species or even widely divergent organisms are called *allelochemic* responses. Eelworm (heterodid) parasites trigger off an unusual plant response which is actually necessary to their survival. They cause cell fusion to occur with the production of giant cells from which the eelworm feeds. The cause of this is not known but it is thought that some plant parasitic nematodes interfere with plant growth hormone ratios. Plant resistance to nematodes is obviously highly important to agriculturalists and horticulturalists and it may be conferred by a single gene, either dominant or recessive. Strains of potato resistant to the potato root eelworm start to produce giant cells but these soon become surrounded by necrotic cells so that development of larval stages is prevented early on and the few that survive become males. It would be interesting to know whether this imbalance in sex ratios was a starvation effect or had some other cause. Cross-resistance also seems to operate in plants and infection by *Meloidogyne incognita*, a root knot nematode, can inhibit simultaneous infections by *Pratylenchus penetrans* in different regions of the same tomato root.

3·9 Summary

The host provides the only environment in which the parasite can survive yet it may be an actively and specifically hostile one. Apart from the physical problem of attachment parasites have to be able to maintain themselves against the host's defence and immune reactions and, if gut parasites, against the action of the host's digestive juices. The extent to which the gut parasite is in control of the situation can be seen by the way that many use bile and pH conditions as triggers for further development (see Chapter 5). Immune responses are particularly well developed in mammalian hosts but invertebrates and other vertebrates show a range of tissue reactions that discourage the establishment of invaders. Such responses range from encapsulation to cell-mediated and humoral antibody responses. Even gut parasites do not escape such protective responses and may be eliminated but the problem is acute for forms that migrate through tissues or actually live in blood or lymph.

The whole history of a host's exposure to disease obviously affects its susceptibility and therefore, at a population level, the epidemiology and population dynamics of its parasites. The picture is further complicated by cross-immunity where infection by one species may render the host resistant to a completely different kind of parasite. As will be seen (Chapter 6) some parasites 'gear' their life cycles to the immunological state of their hosts and may concentrate their main reproductive activity to, for example, young animals which have not yet become immune or reproductively active hosts whose hormones temporarily suppress the immune response.

4 Feeding and Respiration

4.1 Feeding

Helminths are heterotrophs and may have quite specific nutritional requirements, evolved perhaps as a consequence of long association with a particular host. One of the many difficulties involved in attempts to culture helminths *in vitro* is in satisfying the often unknown nutritional requirements of the parasites and in finding media that have the right balance of nutrients including essential amino acids and vitamin-like substances. Feeding may also involve complex behaviour patterns initiated by particular chemical and physical stimuli such as taste, texture of substrate, feeding position and temperature.

4.1.1 Feeding in gut parasites

Although the small intestine is the preferred site for most gut parasitic helminths there are examples of species living in other regions in various hosts; for example the nematode *Proleptus obtusus* in the stomach of dogfish, the pinworm *Leidynema* sp. in the hind gut of cockroach, the pinworm *Enterobius vermicularis* in the caecum and rectum of man. Most of these sites are colonized by forms that feed on tissues or ingest gut contents directly and do not rely on nutrient uptake across the body wall. Many intestinal helminths probably feed on a mixture of mucosal cells, mucus, semi-digested gut contents and, if they penetrate deep into the mucosa, blood. Some worms cause a great deal of damage to the gut wall, especially those that secrete digestive enzymes directly onto the mucosa.

Digeneans and nematodes feed mainly using their guts which produce a variety of digestive enzymes. In addition there is evidence that adult digeneans such as *Schistosoma* and *Fasciola* can absorb labelled nutrients (e.g. glucose and amino acids) across their body surfaces by mediated transport. Electron microscope work has shown that, far from being an inert, secreted cuticle, the body covering of digeneans is a continuous layer of living syncytial cytoplasm containing mitochondria and secretory inclusions which is in connection with nucleated cell bodies in the parenchyma. Sporocyst stages in molluscs have no gut and those investigated have been shown to absorb nutrients across the tegument, so it would not be surprising if this ability was retained in the adult flukes. Nematodes do have a secreted cuticle and feed mainly with the gut (except for certain forms living in fungus flies which have lost the cuticle and have a naked, absorptive microvillous surface). The mouth structure and pharynx are appropriately adapted to the particular diet, whether it be semi-liquid host gut contents (as in *Ascaris*), mucosal tissues (as in *Trichiuris*, the whipworm) or blood or other tissue fluids (hookworms). In the case of tissue feeders, the mouth may contain stylets or cutting plates.

The tapeworms and acanthocephalans have no gut at any stage of their development and this appears to be an adaptation to the adults parasitizing the intestines of their hosts. Members of both groups absorb soluble foods over the body wall directly into the tissues and the parasite interface can be thought of as being in direct competition with host gut cells for nutrient absorption. The covering layers of tapeworms and acanthocephalans are specialized for absorption in different ways, as reviewed by LUMSDEN (1975). The tapeworm body surface is similar to that already described for digeneans except that the free surface is covered with cytoplasmic processes called microtriches (Figs 4–1a and 4–2). These

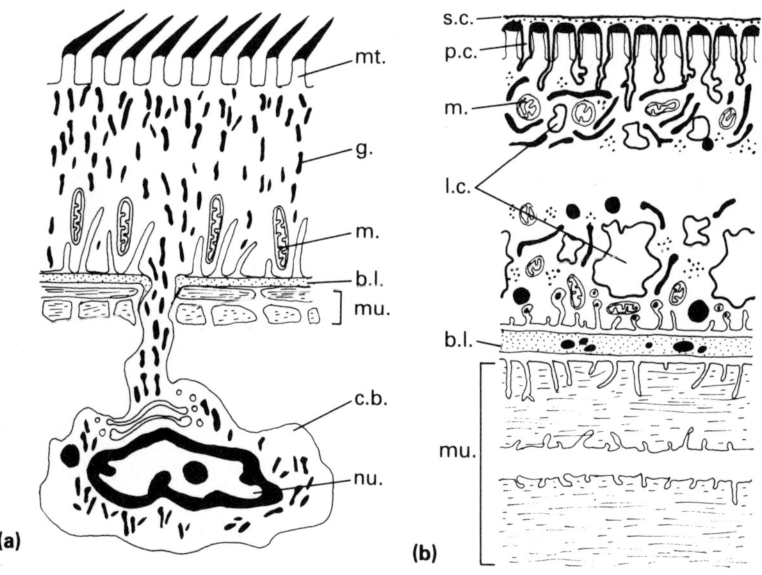

Fig. 4–1 Fine structure of the body wall of (**a**) a tapeworm showing the microtriches and (**b**) of the acanthocephalan *Polymorphus minutus* showing pore-canals. b.l. – basement lamina; c.b. – cell body; g. – granule; l.c. – lacunar channel; m. – mitochondrion; mt. – microthrix; mu. – body wall muscles; nu. – nucleus; p.c. – pore-canal; s.c. – surface coat. ((**b**) from CROMPTON, D. W. T. and LEE, D. L. (1965). *Parasitology*, 55, 357–64.)

measure about 0.8 × 2.0 μm and are similar to the microvilli of host gut cells except that they terminate in a spine-like structure. They presumably increase the membrane surface area available for absorption and the spine-like tips could be adhesive and/or protective. Microthrix densities

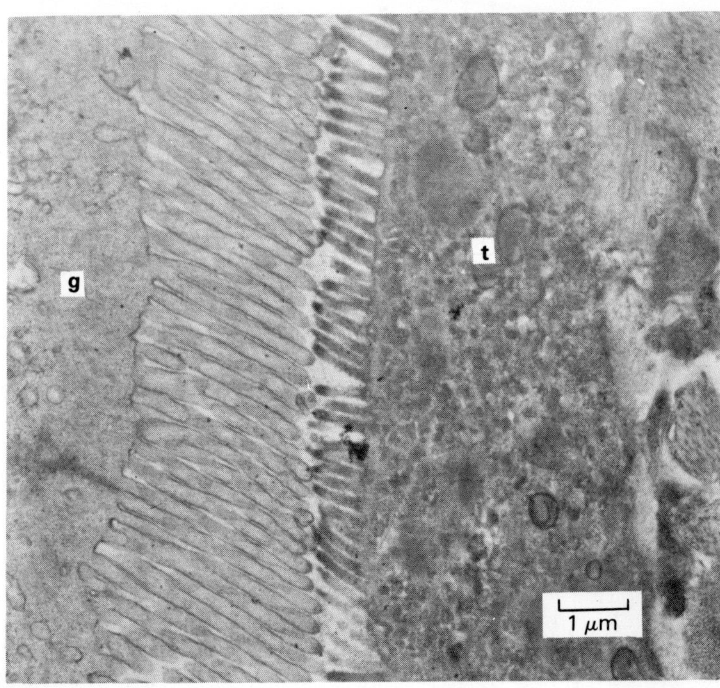

Fig. 4–2 Transmission electron micrograph of the neck region of *Acanthobothrium quadripartitum* in close contact with the surface of a villus in the intestine of its host *Raia naevus*. Note the similarity between tapeworm microtriches (t) (with dense tips) and (paler) host gut microvilli (g). (From McVICAR, A. H. (1972). *Parasitology*, 65, 77–88.)

range from 55/μm^2 on the general scolex surface to 48/μm^2 on the surface of a mature proglottid of *Hymenolepsis diminuta*. The proximal microthrix surface may also provide an extended digestive surface and the tegument of *H. diminuta* (about which most is known) is able to hydrolyse various substrates. This could provide an obvious advantage in releasing small molecules for absorption close to the body surface, perhaps making competition with the host mucosa more efficient, although recent views on vertebrate intestinal cells suggest that there too some digestion occurs in the outer plasma membrane. In addition to producing its own (intrinsic) enzymes such as phosphatases that may hydrolyse glucose-6-phosphate releasing glucose prior to uptake, tapeworms may be able to capture and adsorb extrinsic host enzymes such as pancreatic amylase, and use these to digest food for their own consumption. This theory of membrane-contact digestion, as adsorption of extrinsic enzymes is called, is still speculative but, as described by SMYTH (1972), the tapeworm surface can be considered as a digestive-absorptive surface rather than as a purely absorptive one.

The movement of food molecules across the tegument by active transport, mediated transport and diffusion has been investigated by many workers using labelled nutrients and biochemical and autoradiographic methods and specific carriers have been demonstrated for the mediated transport of particular sugars, amino acids, short and long chain fatty acids, thiamine and riboflavin in *H. diminuta*. Uptake by pinocytosis has not, however, been demonstrated. With regard to vitamins, the broad tapeworm of man, *Diphyllobothrium latum*, has a particularly high vitamin B_{12} requirement and secretes a releasing factor that separates the vitamin from host intrinsic factor. Man cannot absorb the vitamin unless it is complexed with intrinsic factor; the parasite can absorb it alone. Infections with this worm can cause anaemia in certain races which are more susceptible to lack of vitamin B_{12}.

Far from simply lying passively in the intestine soaking up nutrients, tapeworms may take active steps to obtain food. Not only may they use the host's own enzymes but they may also manipulate conditions in the intestine more subtly in their favour. PODESTA and METTRICK (1975) have shown that the jejunum of rats infected with *Hymenolepis* is more acid (pH 5.82–6.28) than the uninfected intestine (pH 6.30–6.60). This may be due partially to secretion of H^+ ions by the worms. Acidification is reported to cut down the rate of fluid and glucose absorption by the host gut whilst enhancing uptake by the worms which may have carriers that work best at low pH. Neither does *Hymenolepis* remain passively attached in one place of the gut but migrates forwards and backwards in the small intestine on a diurnal basis depending on the feeding pattern of the host. Rats are nocturnal and feed most actively between 20.00 and 08.00 h. The tapeworms apparently move forward during the night to meet incoming food, then follow the food back down the gut. Not only is the scolex and whole body moved but the body (up to 70 cm in length) also contracts and extends. Reversal of the host's feeding pattern causes eventual reversal of the worm's activity. It is not known whether this occurs in other tapeworms but a similar migration has been recorded for *Ascaris lumbricoides*.

The rat tapeworm competes with the acanthocephalan parasite *Moniliformis dubius* for the most favourable attachment site just behind the stomach, in double infections. Both helminths feed in a similar manner and both tend to migrate forward as they mature (in addition to the diurnal migration of *Hymenolepis*), perhaps to compensate for elongation of their bodies out of the most favourable zone. Production of ethyl alcohol by the acanthocephalan as an excretory waste may displace the tapeworm competitor.

The body wall of acanthocephalans is modified for nutrient uptake in a different way from that of tapeworms. Its surface area is increased not by microtriches but by infoldings, the pore-canals. These run down into a thick outer layer of syncytial nucleated cytoplasm strengthened internally by fibre layers which resembles a cuticle but in fact is a living layer. The ends of the pore-canals are in contact with pinocytotic-type vesicles although pinocytosis has not been demonstrated. The surface membrane of the tegument is covered with extracellular material resembling a glycocalyx (Fig. 4–1b). Various digestive enzymes have been demonstrated in the walls of the pore-canals so the tegument may again be a digestive-absorptive surface. Despite the fact that the presoma or proboscis region is often buried in host tissue, the metasoma is the main absorptive region and has been shown to absorb labelled fat (^{3}H-glyceryl trioleate) in *Acanthocephalus ranae*, and labelled glucose, tyrosine and thymidine in *Paulisentis fractus*.

4.1.2 *Blood feeding*

Blood feeding may involve one or more of the following specialized features:

(1) cutting or piercing mouthparts,
(2) secretion of anticoagulant,
(3) fluid-pumping device,
(4) possession of bacterial gut symbionts to compensate for a lack of B vitamins in blood,
(5) devices for elimination of sodium, in which blood is rich,
(6) devices for eliminating excess iron,
(7) ability to absorb oxygen from ingested blood across the gut wall.

Unless a parasite lives in the blood such as the blood fluke *Schistosoma*, it may need special devices for penetrating host tissues to obtain blood. The human hookworms *Ancylostoma duodenale* and *Necator americanus* have cutting mouth plates which lacerate a plug of host gut mucosa drawn into the mouth. These nematodes secrete an anticoagulant to ensure continuous flow of blood. *A. duodenale* consumes 0.2 ml blood/day/worm, much of which passes undigested through the gut and it has been suggested that the worms use blood as an oxygen supply as well as for food. There has been some controversy over whether certain tissue parasites are primarily blood feeders. Methods used to investigate this are as follows: (1) demonstration of blood cells in the gut; (2) histochemical demonstration of iron and haematin in the gut; (3) demonstration of the fate of host red blood cells that have been labelled with ^{51}Cr or ^{59}Fe.

4.1.3 *Feeding in plant parasitic nematodes*

All plant parasitic nematodes have stylets for penetration through or between cell walls and these are particularly long and flexible in ectoparasites. The initial penetration into stems and leaves by endoparasites may be via stomata, the larvae migrating along a carbon dioxide gradient. There is much variation in feeding mechanisms; some plant parasitic nematods pierce cells and suck out the fluid contents, whilst others feed on the pectins between cells. Of the cell-content feeders, some feed on the same cell for several days or even throughout their life whilst others are more mobile and soon move on to other cells. Those that are more or less sedentary may cause a specialist response, that of a giant cell formation, and feed off the contents of a mass of fused cells. The root parasitic heteroderids do this. Various types of plant parasitic nematodes affect specific organs and some are stem and leaf parasites whilst others invade the phloem, roots, or apical meristems.

4.2 Respiration

Parasitic helminths show considerable plasticity in adapting their respiratory metabolism to the amount of oxygen available and, like most organisms, have pathways that allow them to respire aerobically or anaerobically. Oxygen tensions vary greatly in various tissue and gut sites within the same host, a fact which affects migratory stages and, if transmission and free-living stages are also taken into account, there is obviously need for considerable metabolic flexibility throughout the life cycle.

Most of the work done on helminth respiration has centred around the intestinal forms, many of which may be exposed to low oxygen tensions and comparatively little is known about the metabolism of tissue parasites or free-living stages. There are tremendous problems in doing biochemical work on parasites since large amounts of material are often required and this may be contaminated with host tissues or with host intestinal flora. Enzyme assays or spectrometric work to identify, for instance, cytochrome systems, may necessitate isolation of purified mitochondrial fractions which are more difficult to prepare than for vertebrate tissues. Also, whole worm homogenates have to be used so that the fraction to be assayed may consist of many types of mitochondrion from different tissues; very different from a homogenous mitochondrion sample from mammalian liver. Alternatively elaborate culture methods may be required, for example, to trace the fate of ^{14}C-glucose via intermediary substances or to investigate the effect of metabolic inhibitors on the various pathways. All too often culture conditions are a mere approximation to the *in vivo* host environment and the parasite may respond artificially to the vastly different conditions or may even be dying slowly.

There can be few niches in hosts where oxygen does not occur , at least in very small amounts, and it is important to point out that many parasites do have an absolute requirement for oxygen which is quite separate from their respiratory requirement for it. Oxygen is needed for oxidizing amino acids, egg production, tanning of egg shells and collagen synthesis. Oxygen may also serve as a metabolic trigger and induce biogenesis of mitochondria and respiratory enzymes during development. It has been suggested, for instance, that oxygen induces cytochrome oxidase activity in the embryonating eggs of *Ascaris*. On the other hand, high oxygen tensions may actually have a harmful effect and the avoidance of high oxygen tensions has been cited as a mechanism keeping the microfilaria larvae of *Wuchereria* in the pre-lung capillaries of man on a diurnal basis (see p. 47).

Until recently it was assumed that the vertebrate gut was more or less anoxic except for the region near the well-vascularized mucosal surface. Previous work on duck intestine using oxygen electrodes suggested there was an oxygen gradient from 25 mm Hg near the wall to 0.5 mm Hg in the centre of the small intestine. Work by PODESTA and METTRICK (1974) has revolutionized these ideas since they found, using a gas sample equilibration method, that most of the rat small intestine has a luminal oxygen tension of 40–50 mm Hg, i.e. similar to that of mammalian venous blood. They also found that the presence of the tapeworm *Hymenolepis diminuta* modifies conditions in the rat intestine and that although anoxic conditions may occur in the unparasitized ileum and colon (due to microflora) they do not occur in the parasitized ileum. This is thought to be due partially to the acidification caused by the tapeworm (p. 29) that makes oxygen more available. So, these authors suggest that sufficient oxygen is available for aerobic respiration in helminths occupying the small intestine. The classic view has been that intestinal worms living in low oxygen tensions use glycolysis to break down glucose to lactate and other organic acids, these often being excreted to avoid paying off the oxygen debt, only parasites buried in the mucosa having enough oxygen available to break down glucose completely using the tricarboxylic acid cycle (TCA cycle).

4.2.1 Respiratory pathways in intestinal worms

Most of the adult intestinal worms that have been investigated biochemically have been found to have in addition to the glycolytic pathway a more or less complete TCA (or Krebs) cycle and cytochrome systems of various types. The presence of TCA cycle enzymes does not necessarily imply aerobic respiration, however, since these could be retained from a developmental stage when aerobic respiration was more important. In addition it may not be widely recognized that certain TCA cycle pathways can be used anaerobically to synthesize organic acids and to reoxidize $NADH_2$ to NAD as well as aerobically in the more conventional way to reduce pyruvate to carbon dioxide and water, a process linked to ATP production. Several parasites have been shown to operate a reversed series of TCA cycle enzyme reactions under anaerobic conditions. This involves using pyruvate or phosphoenol pyruvate to fix carbon dioxide to yield malate or oxaloacetate which is then converted to fumarate. It is known that fumarate can substitute for oxygen in functioning as a hydrogen acceptor for the oxidation of $NADH_2$, being converted to succinate in the process. The latter is then excreted, either directly or after conversion to other organic acids (Fig. 4–3). This reversal can also occur in other invertebrates and in mammals depending on substrate-product concentrations and the amount of oxygen available. In mammals the same enzyme (succinic dehydrogenase) can reversibly catalyse the fumarate$\rightleftharpoons$succinate transformation; it is not known whether more than one enzyme is involved in parasite cells. So this TCA cycle pathway can act as both an oxidizing and reducing system.

4.2.2 *Electron transport systems*

Cytochrome systems have been discovered in a number of parasitic helminths by spectroscopic means. In some, the cytochrome system is present only in a reduced form. *Schistosoma mansoni*, for example, despite its blood-living habit, seems to be largely anaerobic and has a cytochrome system calculated to account for no more than 10% of its respiratory energy. This worm excretes largely lactate. BRYANT (1970) has suggested the mammalian type of electron transport chain ending in cytochrome oxidase may be efficient only at minimum oxygen tensions of 5 mm Hg and although oxygen tensions in the gut may be 30 mm HG and above, many intestinal worms seem to operate an alternative 'anaerobic' pathway ending in fumarate, as already mentioned (p. 32). This would enable the parasite to switch from one pathway to another, depending on the amount of oxygen available.

Similar kinds of branching electron chains have been described for several nematodes and cestodes and may also occur in other invertebrates (e.g. inter-tidal bivalves) as an adaptation to enforced, temporary anaerobic conditions. The cytochrome system may vary throughout the life cycle of parasites and larval stages of *Ascaris* may employ a more complex system than the adult.

4.2.3 *Carbon dioxide fixation*

As described above, intestinal helminths appear to be able to take advantage of the high partial pressure of carbon dioxide (pCO_2) in the gut lumen (250–500 mm Hg) resulting from the action of acid chyme on pancreatic bicarbonate. They fix the carbon dioxide in two principal ways; either combining it with phosphoenol pyruvate (PEP) using the enzyme phosphoenol pyruvate carboxykinase, into oxaloacetate, or by combining it with pyruvate to form malate using 'malic enzyme' (Fig. 4–3). In addition, as BRYANT (1975) has described, carbon dioxide fixation may play a part in carbohydrate synthesis. *Hymenolepis diminuta* was shown to incorporate radiocarbon from $NaH^{14}CO_3$ into polysaccharide. Fixation of carbon dioxide has also been reported in the ectoparasitic monogenean *Entobdella bumpusii* which lives on the skin of sting rays and

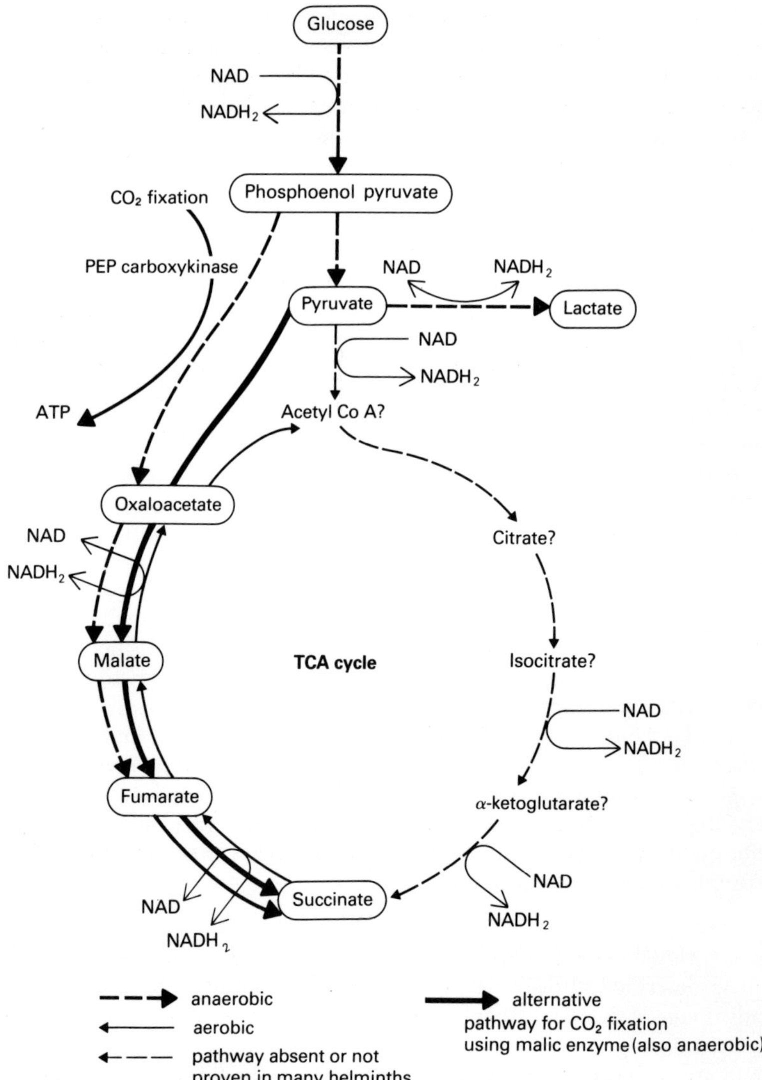

Fig. 4–3 Aerobic and anaerobic respiratory pathways used by intestinal helminths according to the amount of oxygen available. (Generalized diagram based on BRYANT, C. (1970). *Adv. Parasit.*, **8**, 139–72 and BRYANT, C. (1975). *Adv. Parasit.*, **13**, 35–69.)

in fish and rabbit testicular tissue and so is not special to partial anaerobes and may simply be a useful method of synthesizing oxaloacetate. Carbon dioxide is also an important metabolic trigger for hatching, exsheathment and excystment of many intestinal helminths (p. 42).

4.2.4 *Oxygen uptake and parasite haemoglobins*

Parasitic helminths have no circulatory system and oxygen is absorbed by diffusion across the body wall and into the tissues. Movement of the pseudocoelomic fluid of nematodes during locomotion may assist oxygen transport. An ectoparasitic monogenean parasite of the sole, *Entobdella soleae* has been found to make undulatory movements to renew supplies of oxygenated water around the body. These movements increase as the oxygen tension of the surrounding medium is decreased (Fig. 4–4). The flat body shape of many platyhelminth parasites facilitates

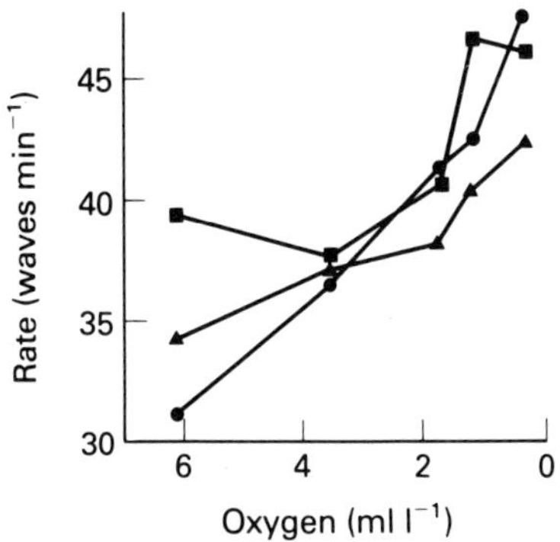

Fig. 4–4 Relationship between the rate of body undulation and the oxygen content of the medium in three separate adult individuals of *Entobdella soleae*. (From KEARN, G. C. (1962). *J. mar. Biol. Ass. U.K.*, 42, 93–104.)

oxygen uptake by providing a large surface area to volume ratio and reducing the distance across which oxygen has to diffuse. Blood-feeding flukes and nematodes may absorb oxygen from their food across their gut walls.

Certain parasitic flukes and nematodes contain their own haemoglobins that differ in absorption spectra, molecular weights and oxygen affinity from those of their hosts. These have not so far been recorded in cestodes and acanthocephalans. The pink colouring of fresh *Ascaris* and *Fasciola* is due largely to their haemoglobins. *Ascaris* has two haemoglobins, one in the body wall and one in the pseudocoelomic fluid. These have a very high affinity for oxygen at low oxygen tensions (low loading tensions); in fact the body fluid haemoglobin has such a high affinity for oxygen it may function more as a myoglobin giving up oxygen only at very low oxygen tensions (see Fig. 4–5). Possibly oxygen flows down an oxygen affinity gradient from outer to inner haemoglobin.

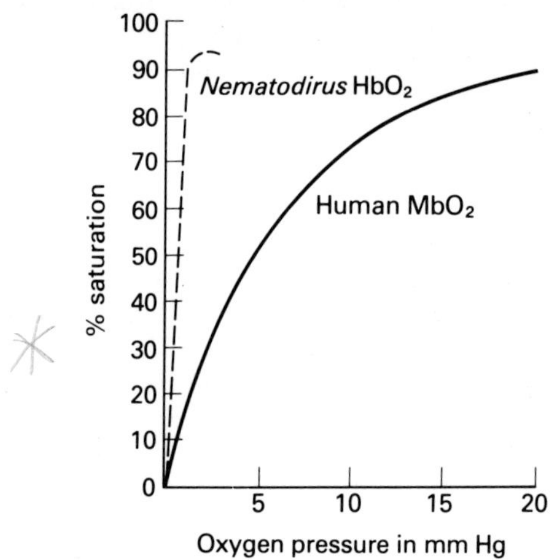

Fig. 4–5 Comparison of the affinity of *Nematodirus* (a ruminant gut parasite) haemoglobin and human myoglobin for oxygen. (From LEE, D. L. (1965). *The Physiology of Nematodes*. Oliver and Boyd, Edinburgh and London.)

Vertebrate haemoglobins give up oxygen when the acidity (due to carbon dioxide concentration) increases (the Bohr effect). Parasite and some invertebrate haemoglobins may show a negative or even reversed Bohr effect: acidity decreasing oxygen release from haemoglobin. This could be an advantage to gut parasites living in conditions of high carbon dioxide and (perhaps) low oxygen tensions since their tissue haemoglobin takes up more oxygen under these conditions than under low carbon dioxide and low oxygen tensions. It must be emphasized that the oxygen obtained may be required not for respiration but for other metabolic processes (e.g. biosynthesis).

4·3 Summary

Parasites, like other organisms, have undergone a marked adaptive radiation in feeding methods, as in other aspects of their biology, to allow them to exploit the various host niches in which they live. Of particular interest are the tapeworms and acanthocephalans which by convergent evolution have lost their mouths and guts and throughout their life history absorb soluble nutrients across a specially modified outer covering. This is an adaptation to living as adults in a specially favoured site of the vertebrate intestine rich in digested foods. These worms are not nearly such passive feeders as has been envisaged and their teguments are specialized digestive-absorptive surfaces that produce their own enzymes or may capture and use host enzymes as well as containing specific carrier and pump mechanisms to facilitate exchanges. Tapeworms in addition may control the pH of the host intestine and thus regulate the efficiency not only of host enzymes but also host carrier mechanisms with which these worms are in competition.

Oxygen availability varies enormously in various gut and tissue sites and oxygen tensions in the small intestine may be higher than has been believed. Parasites have an absolute biosynthetic requirement for oxygen apart from their possible need for it in respiration. In general it seems most helminths are facultatively aerobic and can switch respiratory pathways according to oxygen availability. This flexibility may partly reflect the fact that parasites with free-living forms in their life history probably use aerobic pathways at some stage in development. Many intestinal helminths have complete Krebs cycle enzyme pathways and interestingly may be able to fix carbon dioxide into carbohydrate by reversing part of the pathway under anaerobic conditions.

Ruses for enhancing oxygen uptake involve use of haemoglobins which operate best in acid conditions (reversed Bohr effect) and acidification of gut contents by tapeworms, said to make both oxygen and carbon dioxide more available.

The metabolic flexibility shown by helminths in response to varying availability of oxygen is not confined to them but exists in other invertebrates (and indeed certain vertebrate tissues).

5 Reproduction and Transmission

5.1 Reproductive strategy

Most helminth parasites rely on cross-fertilization to maintain the genetic flexibility in their offspring that is needed for the organism to adapt rapidly to new host strains, and self-fertilization in hermaphrodites is probably quite rare. Nematode and acanthocephalan parasites tend to have separate sexes, although plant parasitic nematodes (and even free-living soil forms) can be hermaphrodites. Platyhelminths including the free-living forms are fundamentally hermaphrodites but *Schistosoma mansoni* is a major exception. Hermaphroditism offers several advantages to parasites and other isolated sessile or sedentary animals (e.g. barnacles) that need a high egg output. Firstly it increases the chances of finding a mate, secondly it increases egg output in that all individuals have egg-producing equipment, thirdly it allows the possibility of self-fertilization as a safety measure if no other worms of the same species are present or even in order to conserve genetic stability for example in specialized helminths 'stranded' in relict hosts. It has also been suggested that hermaphroditism could lead to rapid expression of useful, mutant, recessive characters since if the mutation occurred early in development of ovaries and testes, both male and female gametes could carry the character which could even be immediately expressed were self-fertilization to occur. As a rule, protandry, that is earlier development of testes than ovaries, favours cross-fertilization and reduces the risk of self-fertilization. Sperms from the co-copulant are stored in a seminal receptacle until the eggs have matured.

Locating a mate in the depths of the small intestine or elsewhere must cause problems and there is some evidence that sex pheromones may be produced. Schistosomes do not develop completely unless pairing occurs. Permanent copulation also occurs in *Syngamus*, the tapeworm of poultry and in *Diplozoon paradoxum*, a monogenean gill parasite of cyprinid fish where actual fusion of reproductive ducts and other tissues occurs. Nematodes show great resourcefulness in reproductive strategy. Some root parasitic nematodes, for instance *Meloidogyne* sp., are capable of parthenogenesis as well as orthodox sexual reproduction. Many plant and insect parasitic nematodes (and indeed free-living soil forms) can adjust their sex ratios to maintain the best balance of biological economy. In low infections mermithid nematodes parasitizing insects all develop into females, in moderate infections more males are produced and in high infections males only are produced. This may be controlled by the amount of food available. Females are more demanding of food supplies to manufacture eggs so there is probably an optimum number that can be successfully supported for a given amount of food. In animal parasitic nematodes a 'self-contained system' operates where the total egg output may be reduced to the same level irrespective of the number of worms present. Male worms tend to be shorter-lived than females and may be eliminated from the host first.

Many, although not all, parasites are very prolific, producing vast numbers of eggs. *Ascaris* and *Fasciola* are both said to lay about 20 000 eggs per day. The broad tapeworm of man, *Diphyllobothrium*, may lay 2×10^6 eggs per day for as long as 15 years. This vast egg output serves to compensate for the difficulties involved in finding suitable hosts and completing the life cycle. Such high fecundity is not peculiar to parasites and occurs in other organisms such as fungi, and also marine organisms with a planktonic dispersal phase. The output of offspring may be further boosted by asexual reproduction in the larval stages. This occurs notably in digeneans in the snail intermediate host, which seems remarkably tolerant to damage inflicted upon its tissues. Single miracidia of *Schistosoma mansoni* infecting a snail may produce 200 000 or more cercariae, although the number does not increase proportionately in infections by several miracidia so some population regulation occurs depending on the resources within the snail. The tapeworm *Echinococcus granulosus* compensates for limited reproduction in its final dog host (the worms are only three proglottids long) by a vast asexual reproduction in the intermediate host (see p. 3).

The overall reproductive output, or biotic potential, depends not only on numbers of eggs laid and asexual reproduction but also on the generation time (see p. 11).

Each of the following has an equivalent reproductive output.

Table 2 Reproductive rates of hypothetical free-living nematodes equivalent to that of *Haemonchus contortus* (assuming a 1 : 1 sex ratio). (From CROFTON, H. D. (1966). *Nematodes*. Hutchinson, London.)

	Generation time in days	*Number of eggs per female*
Hypothetical	3	5
	5	9
	7	20
	14	200
	21	2 000
Haemonchus contortus	28	10 000

Accurate estimations of parasite fecundity are very difficult because this varies according to such factors as season, age of host and its immunological response.

5.2 Leaving the host

The main exit routes used by the transmission stages when vacating their definitive host are the gut and other natural ducts such as the tracheae, ureters or reproductive ducts. Stages passing out through the gut have to be protected against digestion by host enzymes or damage by membrane-active surfactants such as bile, and proteinaceous egg shells are usually stabilized by quinone-bonding or keratinization, or even both. The egg of *Ascaris* consists of an outer layer of lipoprotein, a middle layer of chitin and quinone tanned and keratinized protein and an inner layer of esterified glycoside known as ascaroside. The embryo secretes most of the egg shell during development, only an outer lipoprotein layer is added by the uterus wall. Not surprisingly, the egg shell of *Ascaris* is highly resistant for it also has to survive external conditions and eggs are reputed to have hatched after long storage in formalin. The so-called egg shell of taeniid tapeworms infecting terrestrial vertebrates, has evolved from the ciliated coracidial covering (embryophore) of ancestral fish tapeworms and becomes modified during development as a series of closely set keratinized blocks. The true egg shell is a thin membraneous outer capsule which is lost early in development. The eggs of taeniids, but not pseudophyllidean fish tapeworms, are shed whilst still enclosed in the uterus of the proglottid. This probably encourages mass infection by contamination of the food of a macrobivorous host and since the proglottids are active, may aid in dispersal (p. 54). Eggs that leave hosts via natural ducts are usually smoothly round or oval and lack the long filaments that characterize the eggs of ectoparasites such as those of monogeneans that float or tangle with weeds or are glued to sand to anchor them to an environment in which they are likely to meet their fish hosts.

Tissue parasites, especially those living in blood or lymph, have difficulty in getting transmission stages to the exterior. Schistosome blood flukes of man live either in pelvic or mesenteric veins and to bore out through the walls of the blood vessels and through the wall of either the bladder or gut respectively, to reach the outside, the fully-embryonated eggs use larval secretions and a large spine as well as microspines on the shell.

The vacating stage is not always an egg. In *Dracunculus*, the Guinea worm of man, L_1 larvae are released through a skin blister when it is wetted. The blister is formed by the female which is parasitic in the lymph system. Filarial worms living in lymphatics and other tissues produce microfilaria larvae that are liberated into the blood and transmitted by mosquitoes. A more unusual method of transmission is placental infection. *Toxocara canis* a nematode parasite of dogs, can infect puppies *in utero*.

5.3 Hatching outside the host

Eggs are laid at different stages of development. Those of *Fasciola* take between 30 and 160 days to develop on the pasture, depending on the temperature, moisture and oxygen conditions, whilst *Schistosoma* eggs are fully-embryonated when laid. Hatching is usually an active process which ensures that it occurs only under appropriate environmental conditions to maximize survival of larval stages. The operculate eggs of *Fasciola* are stimulated to hatch by light. The enclosed miracidium which has a pair of pigmented eye spots apparently secretes a hatching enzyme that acts on the opercular seal from the inside. The hatching mechanism of schistosome eggs which have no operculum is not known, but one of the chief stimuli for hatching appears to be dilution of the urine or faeces in which the eggs are liberated from the host into water. Hatching is inhibited by 0.8% NaCl and does not occur until dilutions of 0.1% NaCl are reached (Fig. 5–1). Furthermore, eggs will not hatch in darkness or at

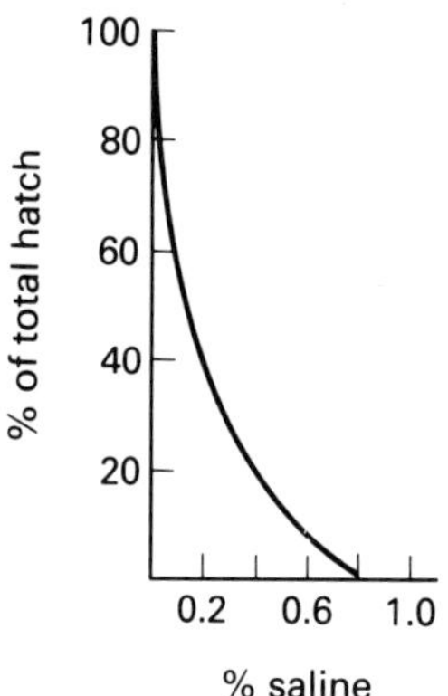

Fig. 5–1 The effect of osmotic pressure on the hatching of eggs of *Schistosoma mansoni* in light at 28°C. (From STANDEN, O. D. (1951). *Trans. Roy. Soc. Trop. Med. Hyg.*, **45**, 225–41.)

temperatures over 37°C, so that hatching is inhibited until the eggs leave the host, ensuring this occurs in optimal conditions for infection of the snail intermediate host.

When *Ascaris* larvae are stimulated to hatch they produce a chitinase, lipase and protease to digest the resistant egg shell. The larva swells to aid its release. Plant parasitic nematodes often require to be activated by specific trigger chemicals released from the appropriate organ of the plant host. Root exudate boosts hatching by *Heterodera* sp. and in *H. rostochiensis*, the potato root eel worm, is stimulated by the glycoside 'solanum' released by the potato into its rhizosphere.

5.4 Passive transmission and physiological triggers

The term passive transmission is rather misleading, since although the infective stage such as the egg or cyst may be acquired passively by the host, the enclosed larva is activated to hatch or excyst by the precise physiological conditions in that host and so responds as actively to the host environment as a skin-penetrating larva. Parasites acquired passively may enter in drinking water as, for example, schistosome cercariae or the Guinea worm *Dracunculus* which infects a small copepod, or contaminatively on food as in *Ascaris lumbricoides* and *Fasciola hepatica*, or whilst encysted in another host as food, for example, *Taenia* spp., *Trichinella spiralis* and *Clonorchis sinensis*. Helminths may also be injected passively into the host by a vector as are the microfilaria larvae of filarial nematodes. Helminths acquired passively by their hosts, especially those that enter via the gut, are usually well protected by a shell, cyst or capsule. The infective L_3 larvae of strongyloid nematodes have a resistant larval sheath which is the unshed cuticle of the L_2 larva. Passive infection depends upon the survival of a resistant larval helminth with a low metabolic rate in a quasi dormant state for long periods. This extends the time that the infective stage has to contact the next host. Metacercarial cysts of *F. hepatica* survive for 130 days around 10°C but only 14 days at 30°C and overwinter on grass in the U.K. Some helminths have escape clauses written into their life cycles, and if by chance they should enter the wrong host by mistake (which must happen very frequently), they can encyst and use that host as a kind of parataenic or accessory host, surviving until eaten by the correct definitive host or hosts. Some acanthocephalans can use this safety measure several times so if eaten by several 'wrong' vertebrate hosts in sequence, along a food chain, will excyst, bore out through the gut wall into the body cavity and re-encyst, in one after another until eaten by a suitable host.

Amongst the most important factors that activate infective stages to hatch, excyst or exsheathe in vertebrate hosts are the following:

(1) increase in temperature on passing into a warm-blooded host,
(2) increased partial pressure of carbon dioxide,
(3) a reducing atmosphere or increased redox potential,
(4) host digestive enzymes to increase the initial, permeability of the eggshell, cyst, etc.,
(5) change in pH,
(6) bile salts.

As reviewed by LACKIE (1975), one or more of these stimuli may be necessary and the stimuli may have to act sequentially in the order each might be encountered on passage through the gut. For example, it may be necessary to pretreat digenean cysts with acid pepsin before exposure to trypsin and bile salts to make them excyst (Fig. 5–2). Less is known about larval activation in invertebrate hosts; however, in some hymenolepid

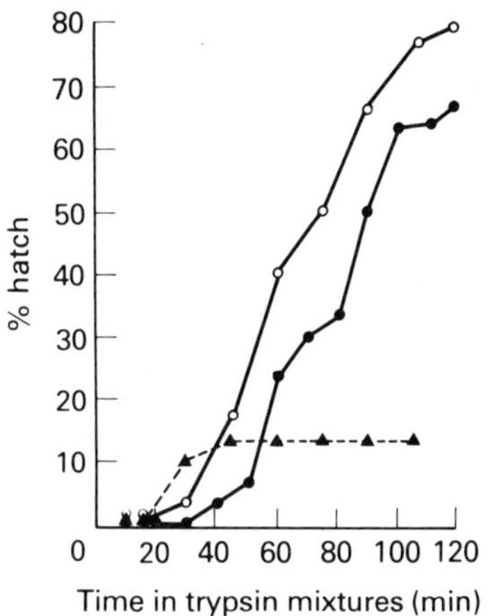

Fig. 5–2 Rates of excystation of *Cyathocotyle bushiensis* metacercaria under different conditions. o——o Cysts pretreated in pepsin – HCl pH 1.05 at 37°C for 15 min followed by incubation in buffered trypsin at pH 7.34 containing 0.5% bile salt. ●——● Buffered trypsin + 0.5% bile salt, pH 7.34. ▲ . . . ▲ Buffered trypsin only, no bile salt, pH 7.34. (From ERASMUS, D. A. and BENNETT, L. J. (1965). *J. Helminthol.*, 39, 185–96.)

tapeworms the egg shell is broken by the digestive action of the arthropod host and the oncosphere is activated simultaneously. Dissolved bicarbonate, carbon dioxide and the action of trypsin at the correct pH all stimulate hatching. High temperature and bile inactivate these eggs destined to hatch in an invertebrate. In the case of *Schistocephalus* a pseudophyllidean bird tapeworm, the stimulus for maturation of the plerocercoid larva is simply a rise in temperature to around 40°C. The eggs of taeniid tapeworms are first acted on by host gut enzymes which soften the shell and then the appropriate host bile is needed to activate the enclosed oncosphere. Bile is an important stimulus to excystment and scolex evagination in many tapeworm cysticercoid and cysticercus larvae, in the activation of many digenean metacercarial cysts and in the excystment of the acanthocephalan *Moniliformis*. It is not always necessary, however, and paradoxically the metacercariae of *Clonorchis sinensis*, the Chinese liver fluke of man, do not need a stimulus from bile to excyst, even though they migrate down the host bile duct. The precise action of bile is not known, but it may act synergistically with lipase to change the permeability of the cyst, and it may even have a more direct effect on muscle contraction since it stimulates activity. The surfactant action alone may be important. Cysticerci of *Taenia pisiformis* can be activated by household detergent. The metacercaria of *Fasciola hepatica* is activated by increased carbon dioxide concentration at 39°C in the presence of a reducing agent but will not excyst even after 24 h unless bile

is added. The cyst of *F. hepatica* consists of several tough resistant layers and is not digested open by host enzymes but the larva is stimulated to secrete excysting enzymes which digest a ventral plug of mucopolysaccharide through which the larva escapes (Figs 5–3 and 5–4). So excystment is very much 'an inside job'.

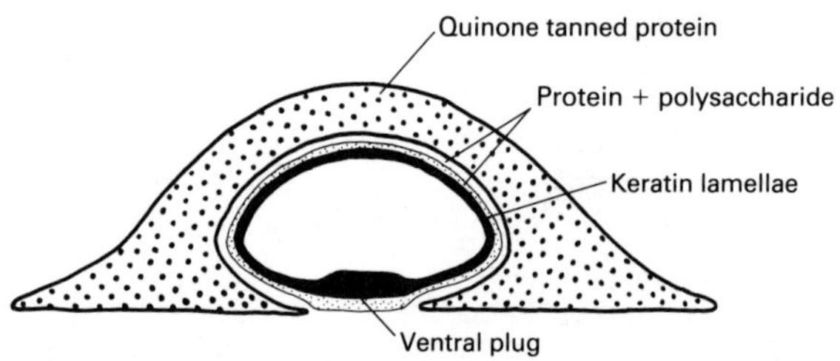

Fig. 5–3 Structure of the metacercarial cyst of *Fasciola hepatica*. The weaker ventral plug region through which the young fluke escapes is shown. (From MERCER, E. H. and DIXON, K. E. (1967). *Z. Zellforsch.*, **77**, 331–44.)

The infective L_3 larvae of strongyloid nematodes are stimulated to exsheathe in their hosts after being swallowed with grass, largely by the increased pCO_2 or undissociated H_2CO_3 under the correct reducing conditions at the appropriate temperature and pH. The latter is important in that it may decide the precise site of exsheathment in the gut. *Haemonchus contortus*, a parasite of the sheep abomasum, exsheathes most rapidly with carbon dioxide stimulus at neutral pH whilst trichostrongyle nematodes inhabiting the sheep's small intestine require carbon dioxide at low pH. Each of these worms is activated by the physico-chemical environment of the organ *prior* to the site in which the adults settle, i.e. in the rumen for *H. contortus* and in the abomasum for the trichostrongyles. These stimuli trigger the release of exsheathing fluid, which may be released via the excretory pore and digests the sheath at a weak point.

5·5 Active transmission and physiological triggers

Transfer between host involving active free-living larval stages necessitates that the behaviour programme of the larval parasites brings them within the host range. This is usually accomplished by a sequence of events whereby the parasite first responds to the general environment in the same way as the host so that the two are likely to meet and then by the operation of directed movements or specific taxes in response to specific host stimuli. The newly-hatched miracidium larva of *Fasciola hepatica* is at first positively phototactic, which brings it to the water surface where its snail host, *Lymnaea truncatula*, lives. The miracidium of *Fasciola gigantica* is negatively phototactic and remains in darker, deeper water where its fully aquatic snail host lives.

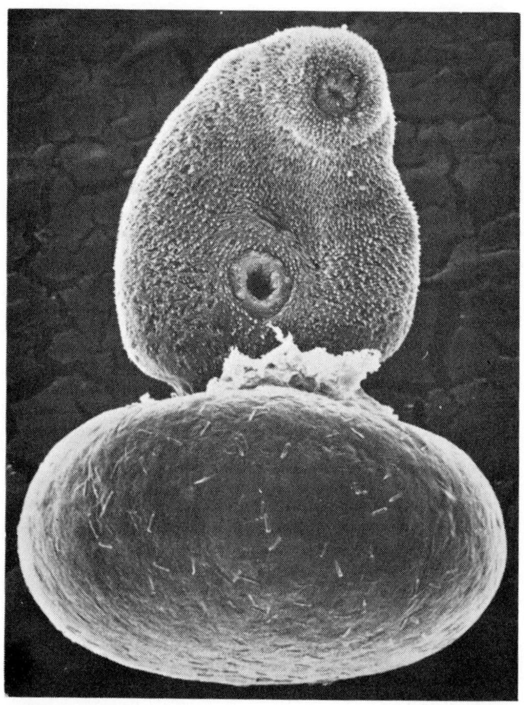

Fig. 5–4 Scanning electron micrograph of *Fasciola hepatica* escaping from its cyst. Note body spines for attachment, penetration and locomotion. × 890 (From BENNETT, C. E. (1975). *J. Parasit.*, **61**, 886–91.)

This general phase of host-habitat location is often followed by a period of apparently random movements when the miracidium swims in long, straight lines, with occasional turns. This may also assist in dispersal. The third phase involves chemotaxis or other directed responses to stimuli produced by snails. The miracidia respond by increasing their speed and rate of turning which keeps them in the vicinity of the host. Snail mucus is attractive to *F. hepatica* miracidia and, short chain fatty acids, in particular, have been shown experimentally to influence their turning behaviour. Miracidia of *Schistosoma mansoni* also show chemical responses to their host snail *Biomphalaria glabrata* and again short chain fatty acids and host amino acids have been shown to influence their swimming behaviour. This was investigated by impregnating snail-sized agar pyramids with known chemicals or host extracts and evaluating miracidial responses to them. Chemical substances in the mucus of sole skin have been shown by KEARN (1967) to play a major role in attracting the highly host-specific larvae of the monogenean fish fluke *Entobdella soleae*.

Cercariae in search of a host show a similar behavioural repertory to miracidia. A period of positive or negative phototaxis may be followed by searching and then attachment. As with miracidia the time span of the dispersal and search phases is strictly limited by the amount of food store in the larval tissues, usually in the form of glycogen in flukes, but lipid in nematodes, and is temperature-dependent. In order to economize on energy output some strigeid cercariae lie resting in the water until disturbed by shadows cast by a fish. They then swim upwards to make contact with the fish. Another cercaria, that of *Azygia lucii*, imitates the mosquito food of the fish by wriggling movements. This attracts fish and the cercaria is able to penetrate their skin and encyst. Cercariae of bird schistosomes are stimulated to penetrate duck skin by the presence of cholesterol in oily skin secretions.

The infective stages of nematodes have to migrate out of the faeces where they were deposited by their final host, usually as eggs, and where the moist warm conditions were favourable for initial development, onto the pasture, where they can encounter their hosts (see p. 54). Phototactic and geotactic responses may be involved in this but no specific taxes have yet been identified to any particular animal host (compare this with plant parasitic forms). Increased activity as the temperature increases may assist in the location of a warm blooded host.

5.6 Summary

The infective stages of parasites, whether active or passive, play a critical role in host location and recognition. Passive infection apparently involves chance infection by dormant resistant stages that undergo an often specific metabolic reawakening in their next host. Active stages tend to be short-lived and undergo a dispersal phase prior to homing in on the host environment. All this necessitates the infective stages having an inbuilt behavioural programme that is unfolded as stimuli, in the host environment and from the host, are encountered in an appropriate sequence. The sensory triggers to each behavioural phase also initiate profound metabolic changes that adapt the parasite to its new environment. The infective L_3 larva of *Haemonchus* may have to change in seconds from being a lipid-metabolizing aerobe living at 10°C to an anaerobe metabolizing glycogen at 37°C when it is eaten from the pasture by its sheep host. The physiological triggers are also developmental triggers and must initiate gene and enzyme switching leading to the onset of a new developmental phase. Although all too little is known at present of the biochemistry of these changes, there is a possibility that when methods of culturing parasites improve these may make good models for investigating the control of differentiation.

6 Dispersal in Time and Space

6.1 Gearing parasite life cycles to those of the host

6.1.1 Diurnal rhythms

Parasites do not, in many cases, reproduce at a constant rate throughout the year but may synchronize their reproductive output with aspects of the biology of their hosts to ensure effective transmission. This can lead to periodic or cyclical phenomena where the actual production, output or behaviour of reproductive stages may show diurnal or seasonal rhythms linked to some biological activity of their hosts (HAWKINS, 1975). As a result the parasite is dispersed in time.

The microfilaria larvae of some tissue-living filarial nematodes show a diurnal behavioural cycle. Adult *Wuchereria bancrofti* live in the deep lymphatics of man and may eventually cause elephantiasis. The blood-living microfilaria larvae are transmitted by *Culex* mosquitoes. It can be shown from blood samples that microfilariae appear in the peripheral blood of man only at night when mosquitoes feed (Fig. 6–1). At other

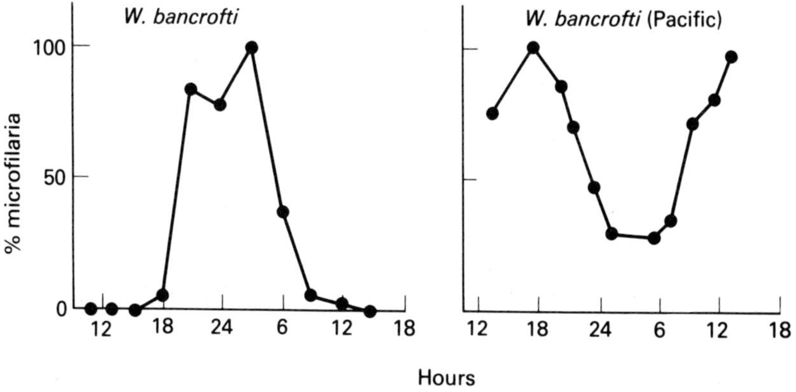

Fig. 6–1 Numbers of microfilariae in the peripheral blood of man at different times of day. *Wuchereria bancrofti* is transmitted by night-biting *Culex* mosquitoes, *W. bancrofti* (Pacific strain) is transmitted by day-biting *Aedes* mosquitoes and has a different periodicity. (From HAWKING, F. (1967). *Proc. Roy. Soc. B.*, **169**, 59–76.)

times they are concentrated in the pre-lung capillaries in venous blood at low oxygen tension which suggests that higher oxygen tensions may in some way be harmful to them. To remain here the microfilariae have to move actively against the current of blood tending to sweep them through the lungs. Reversal of the host's activity regime reverses the appearance of microfilariae in the blood, for these take physiological clues from the host's diurnal rhythm and are apparently sensitive to changes in the *difference* in oxygen concentration across pre- and post-lung capillaries. Interestingly, a strain of *Wuchereria bancrofti* occurring in the Pacific Islands is transmitted by day-biting *Aedes* mosquitoes, and the microfilariae of this parasite appear in the blood diurnally but with a less marked rhythm than nocturnally transmitted strains (Fig. 6–1).

The mature female pinworm of man, *Enterobius vermicularis* (a nematode) which lives in the caecum and rectum, migrates out of the anus at night to lay eggs on the surrounding skin. This causes severe itching in children, the main sufferers of pinworm, but only between 21.00 and 24.00 h. By this behaviour the worms avoid faecal contamination of the eggs which are then free to be dispersed on clothes or by blowing around. The itching causes scratching and eggs are also transmitted under the finger nails. The rat, which is nocturnal, has a pinworm, *Syphacia muris*, which does the reverse, that is it lays its eggs during the day when the rat is quiescent. This is an adaptation that keeps the eggs in the nest.

The output of cercariae from snails may also vary periodically. Under natural conditions in South Africa the cercariae of *Schistosoma mansoni* and *S. haematobium* are liberated from their respective snail hosts between 11.00 and 14.00 h when man is more likely to enter the water for washing and bathing. Rodent strains of *S. japonicum* release their cercariae at dusk when rodent activity is greatest. The eggs of the monogenean fluke *Entobdella soleae* show periodicity in hatching and the maximum hatch occurs just after dawn. At this time the sole host has ceased its nocturnal activities and has come to rest on the sea-bed. By hatching early the worm has all day to catch the fish! The parasite clock is set by exposure to alternating periods of light and darkness during development and eggs reared totally in darkness show no response.

6.1.2 Seasonal rhythms – response to host reproductive cycles

Parasites may need to concentrate their reproductive activities to a time of year when their hosts reproduce since infection may occur more easily when hosts gather to breed. Alternatively, some parasites can infect only young hosts, because of immunity or other factors. The monogenean bladder parasite *Polystoma integerrimum* normally infects frogs at the tadpole stage only. To ensure that oncomiracidia occur at the same time as tadpoles, reproduction in *Polystoma* is triggered by host sex hormones so the parasite is stimulated to lay eggs at the same time as frogs produce eggs and sperm. Indeed, maturation of the parasites can be induced experimentally by injecting infected frogs with pituitary extracts. The development time of the eggs is also geared to that of the host spawn and ciliated larvae hatch at the time the first batch of internal gill stage tadpoles occur and infect these via the mouth. If a larva infects an external gill stage tadpole, a remarkable thing happens and some trophic response causes a neotenic generation of parasites to be produced that lay eggs within about twenty days instead of the usual three years it takes the bladder parasites to come to maturity. Larvae hatching from these eggs infect late internal gill stage tadpoles, so the life cycle has an escape clause written into it. Physiological strains of *P. integerrimum* exist where neotenic forms are more common and this occurs in warmer regions. Because of the migratory spawning habits of their hosts, many fish parasitic monogeneans also synchronize their reproductive activity with the seasonal reproductive activity of their hosts. The coordinating factor is not known but it may be a common response of host and parasite to changing temperature and day length.

The population dynamics of many kinds of sheep and cattle nematodes are also influenced by the biology of their hosts and this is the result of a complex interaction of factors including the host immune response and external climatic factors acting on the free-living infective stages. RATCLIFFE *et al.* (1969) suggest that populations of the stomach worm *Haemonchus contortus* in the sheep are regulated to control the parasite's effect on the host and to prevent overcrowding. Young lambs produced in spring are susceptible to infection with *H. contortus* and worms develop to maturity and produce eggs which pass out in the faeces onto the pasture and reinfect them. As the population continues to increase the large worm burden stimulates the immune response of the host and by autumn, egg output decreases due to this response. Further infections at this stage do not develop as far as adults but are inhibited in an inactive state within the sheep. The eggs laid onto the pasture from adult worms do not overwinter well and the parasite overwinters in the host. The following spring the infected ewes give birth and, due to hormonal factors, their immunological response declines for a period. This removes the negative feed-back brake on growth of the worm burden and the inhibited juvenile worms that overwintered in the ewes are able to resume development. Thus an increased number of eggs is produced, called the spring or post-parturient rise. These eggs develop into larvae that mainly infect lambs, since the immunological response of the adult sheep is rapidly regained after birth. The whole cycle then begins again and is controlled by the host immune response linked to its reproductive cycle. A similar kind of population regulation has been shown to operate for other nematodes of grazing animals (MICHAEL, 1976).

6.1.3 *Host behaviour induced by parasites*

Apart from synchrony with host behaviour and life cycle, another example of the finesse of the evolutionary fit between parasites and their hosts is that apparently passive infective stages in intermediate hosts can adjust the behaviour of those hosts so as to make them more likely to be eaten by the definitive host.

An amazing example of this phenomenon is the behaviour of the sporocyst of *Distomum macrostomum* (syn. *Leucochloridium paradoxum*) in its snail host, *Succinea* sp. (see HOLMES and BETHEL, 1972). The sporocysts contain encysted metacercariae and are brightly banded with green or brown. By day they migrate into the thin-walled snail tentacles which they distend and make very conspicuous (Fig. 6–2). The sporocysts also

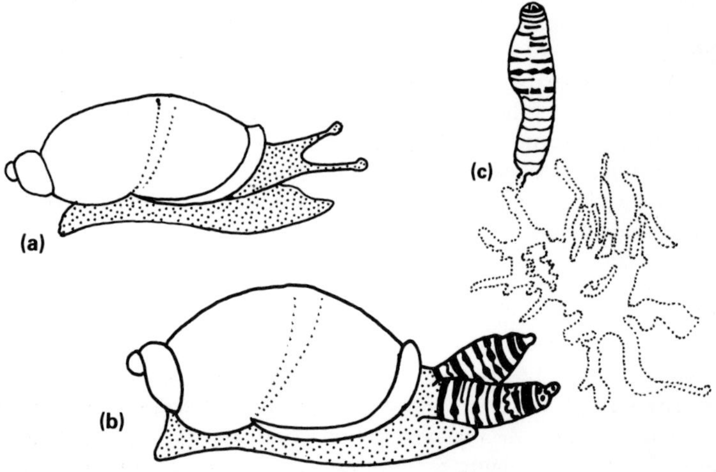

Fig. 6–2 The effect of a parasite on its host. Banded sporocysts of the fluke *Distomum* (=*Leucochloridium*) make their snail host (*Succinea* sp.) very conspicuous so transmission to bird predators is enhanced. (**a**) Uninfected snail, (**b**) infected snail, (**c**) sporocyst dissected out. (Drawn from photographs in BAER, J. G. (1971). *Animal Parasites*. Weidenfeld and Nicolson, London.)

pulsate, giving the snail the appearance of a flashing beacon to some hungry thrush, the main definitive host. Infected snails also change their normally cryptic behaviour and migrate out onto the upper leaf surfaces, further increasing their chances of being eaten, instead of remaining hidden below. During the night, sporocysts migrate back into the body of the snail.

The metacercariae of the lancet liver fluke, *Dicrocoelium*, of sheep and cattle have an equally unlikely effect on their second intermediate host, the field ant. The ant eats cercariae emerging from land snails in the form of 'slime balls' and the first one or two cercariae to reach the suboesophageal ganglion of the ant's brain encyst there, the remainder encysting in other tissues. The behaviour of an infected ant is modified so that it tends to crawl to the tip of a grass blade and at low temperatures in the evening until morning grips the blade firmly with its mandibles and is unable to release its grip until the temperature rises during the day. The infected ants are thus exposed to the host at grazing times.

The parasite may also increase its chances of transmission simply by disabling the intermediate host and making it easier prey. Strigeid metacercaria live in the eyes of fish where they may cause partial or complete blindness, but only in heavy infections. In natural circumstances the older hosts, which have been exposed longer to parasite attack, are, presumably, the most severely disabled. The coenuri of the tapeworm *Taenia multiceps* develop in the brain and spinal cord of sheep and other ruminants producing 'Gid', a disease characterized by staggering and loss of coordination, so that infected animals fall behind the herd and are more easily predated. The plerocercoids of *Schistocephalus* distort the abdomens of sticklebacks and disrupt their silvery reflective camouflage mechanism since flashes from their protruding silvery bellies can be seen from above by a predatory bird. The enormous larval tapeworm burden also slows them down.

6.2 Population dynamics of parasites and hosts

6.2.1 General factors

Space permits only an outline of the principles involved; for further reading see KENNEDY (1975). The ecological factors that govern the changes in the host-parasite population balance are complex and act at various levels. The parasite population size is related to the population size and density of the intermediate and final (plus possible other) hosts involved in its life cycle. This is controlled in turn by climatic and seasonal factors, availability of food and water, predation, disease and the general balance between reproductive rate and mortality. These factors act not only on the host population size but on their physiological state, determining their availability for infection. If the input of food decreases, input of encysted infective stages decreases, host health deteriorates and parasites may be eliminated from the gut or cease laying eggs in starved hosts. On the other hand, in another situation, a tissue parasite may find it easier to invade a starved host if it is unable to mount a protective immunological response as a result. The factors so far outlined may produce different host-parasite models. Climatic factors also directly affect the survival and rate of development of the free-living stages of parasites.

Factors that determine whether a host is available for infection are diet, host behaviour (including migration and hibernation), general physiological condition, host immunity and host age (Fig. 6–3). The last two factors may be related. A combination of these interacting factors determines whether hosts fall into one of three main categories: 'infecteds' which carry the infection, 'susceptibles' which are open to infection but not yet infected, and 'removeds' which for various reasons

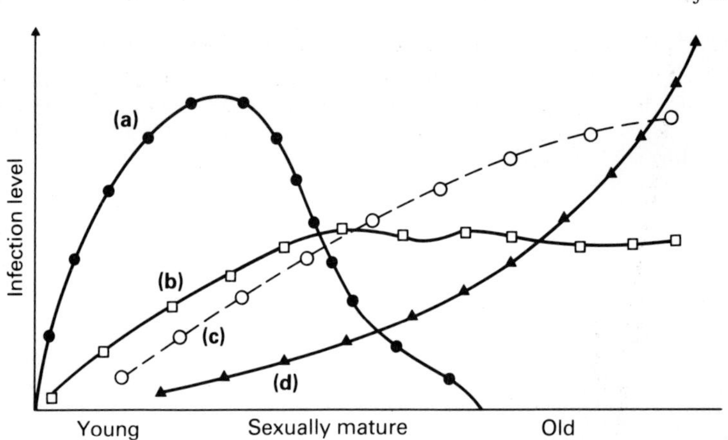

Fig. 6–3 Patterns of parasitic incidence as influenced by host age. (**a**) Infection typical in young hosts; (**b**) parasite short-lived; equilibrium established between parasite loss and recruitment; (**c**) parasites reduce the chance of host survival; (**d**) parasite long-lived, non-pathogenic. (From CROLL, N. A. (1973). *Parasitic and Other Associations*. Pitman Medical, London.)

are not exposed to infection. 'Removeds' may be either genetically insusceptible to infection, since there exists considerable variation to susceptibility to infection within host populations, or may be immunologically susceptible but may have a different diet or behaviour that isolates them from the parasite, again perhaps in an age- or sex-related way. The incidence of the tapeworm *Proteocephalus percae* in perch decreases with the age of perch because the fish moves from feeding on plankton where it contacts larval stages of the parasite to eating fish. As an example of sex-related behaviour determining parasite distribution, the incidence of the lung fluke *Paragonimus* in West Africa is restricted to a small area where it is believed that eating undercooked fresh-water crabs (infected with metacercariae) increases the fertility of adolescent girls. Women are much more highly infected here than men.

A particular type of seasonal and age-linked behavioural pattern is the migration of some species for feeding or breeding purposes and this may influence the epidemiology (i.e. pattern of spread) of their parasites. A clear-cut example of this is provided by fish that migrate from fresh water to the sea or vice versa. Young salmon born in fresh water have at first a fresh-water parasite fauna but this is shed and replaced by marine parasites when the salmon migrate out to sea. When salmon return on their spawning run their marine parasites are lost and this is due partially to the fact that the hosts do not feed at this time.

6.2.2 *The negative binomial frequency distribution of parasites in hosts*

Parasites are not distributed evenly through a host population even within a host age group. A random distribution would be expected to give a frequency distribution of pattern shown in Fig. 6–4a which can be described by the Poisson model. In fact distribution is not random and if the frequency distribution is plotted for the numbers of parasites in individual hosts, an overdispersed distribution that can be interpreted as a negative binomial distribution results (Fig. 6–4b). This means that most

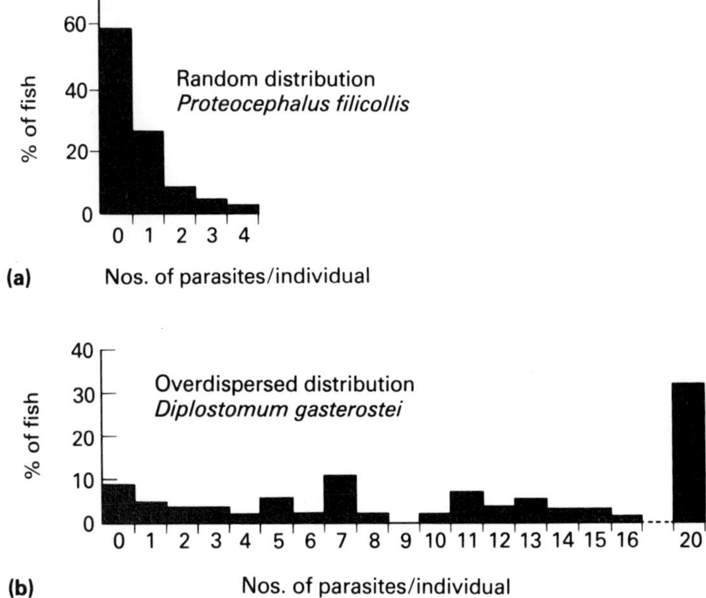

Fig. 6–4 Frequency distributions of parasites in their hosts. (**a**) Hypothetical graph showing random distribution according to the Poisson model. (**b**) Actual overdispersed distribution of diplostomulum larvae in the eyes of sticklebacks (negative binomial model). ((**b**) from PENNYCUICK, L. (1971). *Parasitology*, **63**, 389–406.)

hosts are uninfected or contain very few parasites and only a few are heavily infected. Figure 6–4b shows the distribution of diplostomulum larvae in the eyes of sticklebacks (the intermediate host for this parasite). This kind of distribution suggests that not all the sticklebacks have an equal chance of becoming infected and this could be interpreted in terms of host differences in innate susceptibility, age, behaviour, sex, feeding preferences, or immune state. This type of distribution could also be obtained if larval stages were not dispersed randomly but mass infect a susceptible host or if a primary infection made it easier for subsequent infections to become established. The negative binomial distribution emphasizes the way that the parasite population as well as the individual parasite is in balance with the host. Only the few heavily infected hosts are likely to be disabled by parasites. Many may carry a low-level infection which is sufficient to maintain the parasite life cycle.

6.3 Dispersal in space

Parasites are dispersed by their own efforts, as in free-living miracidia, oncomiracidia, cercariae and larval nematodes and by the actions of their vectors and intermediate hosts. Gut parasites expelled in the faeces of their host have the particular problem that their hosts will not graze around the faecal pat so they have to migrate out onto the pasture. The disassociated proglottids of *Taenia taeniaeformis*, the beef tapeworm, perform this migration. Larvae of the cattle lungworm *Dictyocaulus viviparus* have evolved a remarkable dispersal mechanism. The larval nematodes crawl up the vertical hypha of the mould fungus *Pilobolus* growing on the cow pat and when they reach the sporangium sit on the darker lid. This is blown off to release the fungal spores explosively and the nematodes are catapulted about 1 m onto the pasture (Fig. 6–5).

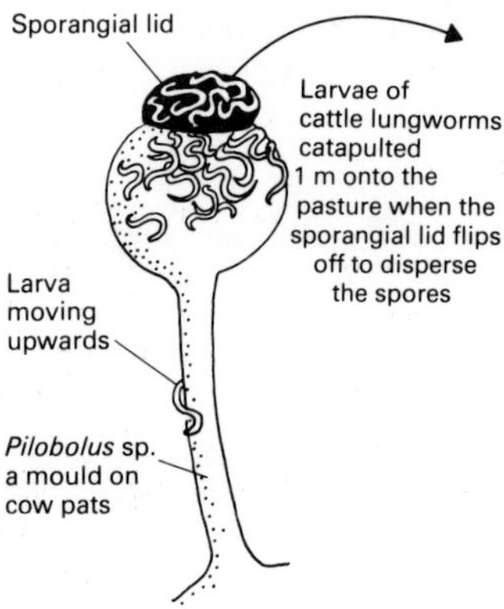

Fig. 6–5 *Dictyocaulus* larvae crawling onto the sporangial lid of the cow pat fungus *Pilobolus*. From here they will be explosively dispersed. (Drawn from a slide given by Professor N. A. Croll.)

Recent work shows that the larvae of other nematode parasites of cows, namely *Cooperia punctata* and *Trichostrongylus colubriformis* may be dispersed in the same way and larvae of *Ostertagia ostertagia* can be transported on the legs of psychodid flies.

Parasites tend to show a clumped dispersal not only in their hosts but also in the macrohabitat that their hosts occupy. Thus although a particular parasite may occur over a wide geographical area it does not have a uniform distribution in this area but is encountered in pockets or foci with the appropriate conditions for survival of parasite and host (see p. 56).

6.4 Summary

The timing of the production and release of transmission stages may be critical to the effective contact between parasite and host populations, especially where the host population density shows diurnal or seasonal variations or when immunologically susceptible hosts (e.g. young ones) only abound at certain times of year. Some remarkable 'solutions' have evolved allowing the parasite to gear the timing of its life cycle and habits to those of the host. The parasite may act upon some physiological clue such as diurnal changes in oxygen concentration or temperature in the host or be influenced by seasonal changes in diet, hormone levels or immunity in order to produce infective stages at a time of day or year when they are most likely to be transmitted successfully. Modification of host behaviour by the parasite may also increase the effectivity of transmission by making the intermediate host more vulnerable to predation. Such evolutionary strategies include making the host more conspicuous, reducing its stamina, disorientating it and changing its behaviour. Unfortunately far too little is known of the nervous basis of this transformation from a cryptic to flamboyant and attractive state.

A parasite may show different kinds of distribution in the intermediate and final hosts although overall there is a tendency for them to show a negative binomial distribution where only a few hosts are heavily infected, and therefore likely to be damaged by the parasite, and most have low-level infections sufficient to maintain the parasite. This shows how the parasite population as much as the individual parasite is in balance with the host. The variables affecting the size of host and parasite populations are extremely complex and in order to study such interactions it is necessary to construct mathematical population models. In this way it may be possible to control disease by predicting what kinds of measures may be most effective at reducing parasite numbers to the 'break point' below which effective transmission cannot occur.

7 Helminth Evolution

Parasite evolution is similar to that of other organisms in that it depends on mutation, recombination, isolation, competition and selection. These processes, of course, act on the whole life cycle since the parasite must be in balance with its environment at each stage.

As already mentioned (p. 8), the long evolutionary association between some parasites and their hosts has led to physiological specificity: particular parasites being unable to survive except in the precise physiological conditions offered by members of one host species or its close relations. In this position the parasite has to 'remain opportunistic and adaptable' in an evolving environment and match its own evolutionary rate to that of its host, so that as the host speciates so does the parasite. On the other hand, a certain amount of conservatism is necessary in parasite evolution to retain the particular assortment of specialized adaptations that fit the parasite to its highly specialized life style. There are many factors controlling the balance between genetic adaptability and conservatism. One factor is the amount of inbreeding or outbreeding within the population, the most extreme form of inbreeding being self-fertilizing hermaphroditism, although this is thought to be rare in helminths. Population size is another important factor affecting gene mixing, since the smaller the population the greater the degree of inbreeding, although intraspecific competition is reduced. The rate of evolutionary change and therefore adaptability also depends upon the generation time of the parasite (see p. 11) and in forms with asexual multiplication stages in their life cycles, such as digenean flukes and echinococcid tapeworms, on the amount of cloning in larval stages. The degree of specificity to various hosts, the longevity of all stages and the effectivity of dispersal mechanisms could also affect the rate at which parasites encounter new hosts or new host strains. A parasite that shows partial compatibility with a new host may very quickly become adapted to it, as outlined below.

In practice an even more important unit than the overall parasite population in evolutionary terms is the individual focus where parasites are concentrated. Parasites often show a discontinuous distribution within their geographical range and occur in local foci where conditions favour their survival; for example, helminths such as schistosomes or filarial nematodes, with aquatic stages in their life history, or aquatic vectors, tend to be centred around water and, in the case of schistosomes, it is the discontinuous distribution of suitable snail habitats that largely determines the positions of the foci. Indeed man, by opening up previously arid regions by means of irrigation schemes such as the Aswan Dam scheme in Egypt, or hydroelectric projects like that at Lake Volta in Ghana, has unwittingly created new disease foci for schistosomiasis by furthering the spread of snail hosts and enhancing contact between man and infected snails. Isolation of foci could provide a basis for the physical separation necessary within a population for reproductive isolation, and eventually speciation, to occur. As described by WRIGHT (1971), the amount of gene flow between the various foci will depend in particular on the mobility of final and intermediate hosts and on the longevity of the parasite in the final host. A man infected with a long-lived, egg-producing parasite can disseminate eggs over a wide area containing many foci. The shorter the life span of the adult parasite, the greater the chance of isolation and eventual speciation occurring. This kind of focal distribution helps to explain why many parasites exist as different strains. Such strains may differ in their ability to infect various hosts, in their pathogenicity, drug resistance, growth rate, time of maturity or egg output. The occurrence of different strains of schistosome adapted to infect different species of snail is immensely important in understanding the spread of schistosomiasis and its control. Those schistosomes with terminal-spined eggs (i.e. *S. haematobium*, *S. bovis*, *S. mattheei*, *S. intercalatum* and *S. leiperi*) use species of *Bulinus* snails as intermediate hosts, but some species are more flexible than others in being able to use more than one snail species, only one species, or even only a particular strain of a snail population. Even if there is only partial compatibility and just a few parasites survive infection in an unusual type of snail host, those that survive will be better adapted to their hosts next time and so new strains, fully adapted to their new host species, may occur in as few as two to three generations. When *Fasciola hepatica*, the liver fluke, was accidentally introduced into Australia in infected domestic livestock, although the normal European snail host *Lymnaea truncatula* was absent, its ecological counterpart, *L. tomentosa*, unfortunately provided a suitable alternative in which it could complete the life cycle. There is now an Australian strain of *F. hepatica* better adapted to *L. tomentosa* than the European strain.

Unlike most flukes, schistosomes have separate sexes. As described by WRIGHT and SOUTHGATE (1976), double infections with different schistosome species in the same host may result in hybridization and the hybrid strains may not only be viable but may also be able to use the intermediate snail hosts of both parental strains, thereby possibly increasing the range of the parasite. For instance, the progeny resulting from crosses between male *S. mattheei* and female *S. intercalatum* were found to be equally infective to both the paternal *Bulinus africanus* group and the maternal *B. forskali* group of snails. This dual infectivity persisted for three generations, even when the parasite was cycled through the paternal snail host only. A natural focus for this hybridization has been found in Cameroon. The already serious schistosome problem in Kenya, caused by the Kariba Lake scheme, now a great tourist centre and breeding ground for snail hosts of *S. haematobium*, could be exacerbated if strains of *S. haematobium* from other parts of Africa were to be introduced. The Kenyan strain of *S. haematobium* uses *B. africanus* group snails as intermediate hosts, but in other areas are strains of this parasite that use *B. truncatus* snails, shown to be prevalent over a wide area of Kenya. Hybridization of the two strains, if the latter were to be introduced, would produce a form that grew more rapidly, produced larger worm burdens and had a larger host range, and would make control even more difficult than it is at present.

Appendix: Projects

The following suggestions involve material not usually considered infective to humans. Some are not entirely original projects but they may generate ideas and enthusiasm for further investigations.

Information about the parasites of common animals may be obtained from the following: **Fish** – CHAPPELL, L. H. (1969). *J. Fish Biol.*, **1**, 137–52 and KENNEDY, C. R. (1974). *J. Fish Biol.*, **6**, 613–44. **Amphibians** – COX, F. E. G. (1971). *J. Biol. Educ.*, **5**, 35–51. **Mammals** (voles and shrews) – LEWIS, J. W. (1968). *J. Zool. Lond.*, **154**, 313–31. **General** (including cercariae in snails) – CANNING, E. U. *et al.* (1973). *Field Studies*, **3**, 681–717.

(a) Investigations on parasite distribution in their hosts

Many parasites have been shown to have a 'negative binomial' type of distribution in their hosts (see p. 53) and this can be investigated for *Polymorphus minutus* (acanthocephalan) in the body cavity of *Gammarus pulex*. The small orange cystacanth is clearly visible through the dorsal body wall of the shrimp. This can also be done on diplostomulid flukes in the lens of fish eyes, or on *Centrorhynchus alucanis* cystacanths (acanthocephalan) in the body cavity of shrews. The effects of host age and season on the distribution can also be investigated bearing in mind that infection levels may vary from year to year.

(b) Effects of parasites on host behaviour or conspicuousness

The behaviour of infected and uninfected forms can be compared. This can easily be done for *Polymorphus* cystacanths in *Gammarus* (other colourless cystacanths could also be present however). Sticklebacks infected with eye flukes or *Schistocephalus* (a large tapeworm plerocercoid larva in the body cavity) might also be good material. The actual degree of infection may have to be decided by dissection after the event. If snails or bivalves (especially seashore forms) are sampled from 'conspicuous' or 'inconspicuous' sites their infection levels may be found to vary significantly.

(c) Parasite competition

The tapeworm *Proteocephalus fillicollis* and the acanthocephalan *Neoechinorhynchus rutili* may both occur in the gut of the three-spined stickleback. Usually *Proteocephalus* is distributed evenly along the intestine but may be displaced forward if the acanthocephalan is present (see CHAPPELL, L. H. (1969) (above)).

(d) Factors affecting transmission

(i) If infected snails are placed in separate beakers of water the time of cercarial emergence can be noted. The effect of light and temperature can then be investigated. (N.B. More than one species of cercaria may be involved and each species may do different things.)

(ii) The behaviour of cercariae (e.g. negatively or postively phototactic) at different times after emergence can be studied (some may simply encyst!).

References

BRYANT, C. (1970). Electron transport in parasitic helminths and protozoa. *Adv. Parasit.*, **8**, 139–72.

BRYANT, C. (1975). Carbon dioxide utilization and the regulation of respiratory metabolic pathways in parasitic helminths. *Adv. Parasit.*, **13**, 35–69.

CARVAJAL, J. and DAILEY, M. D. (1975). Three new species of *Echeneibothrium* (Cestoda, Tetraphyllidea) from the skate *Raja chilensis* Guchenot, 1848, with comments on their mode of attachment and host specificity. *J. Parasit.*, **61**, 89–94.

CLEGG, J. A. (1972). Functional aspects of parasite surfaces. *Symp. Brit. Soc. Parasit.*, **10**, 23–40.

HAWKING, F. (1975). Circadian and other rhythms of parasites. *Adv. Parasit.*, **13**, 123–82.

HOLMES, J. C. and BETHEL, W. M. (1972). Modifications of intermediate host behaviour by parasites. In: Behavioural aspects of parasite transmission. *Zool. J. Linn. Soc.*, **51**, 123–49.

KEARN, G. C. (1967). Experiments on host finding and host-specificity in the monogenean skin parasite *Entobdella soleae*. *Parasitology*, **57**, 585–605.

KENNEDY, C. R. (1975). *Ecological Animal Parasitology*. Blackwell, Oxford.

LACKIE, A. M. (1975). The activation of infective stages of endoparasites of vertebrates. *Biol. Rev.*, **50**, 285–325.

LLEWELLYN, J. (1956). The host specificity, micro-ecology, adhesive attitudes and comparative morphology of some trematode gill parasites. *J. mar. Biol. Ass. U.K.*, **35**, 113–27.

LUMSDEN, R. D. (1975). Surface ultrastructure and cytochemistry of parasitic helminths. *Exp. Parasit.*, **37**, 267–339.

MICHAEL, J. F. (1976). The epidemiology and control of some nematode infections in grazing animals. *Adv. Parasit.*, **14**, 355–97.

PODESTA, R. B. and METTRICK, D. F. (1974). Pathophysiology of cestode infections: effect of *Hymenolepis diminuta* on oxygen tension, pH and gastrointestinal function. *Int. J. Parasit.*, **4**, 277–92.

PODESTA, R. B. and METTRICK, D. F. (1975). *Hymenolepis diminuta:* Acidification and bicarbonate absorption in the rat intestine. *Exp. Parasit.*, **37**, 1–14.

RATCLIFFE, L. H., TAYLOR, H. M., WHITLOCK, J. H. and LYNN, W. R. (1969). Systems analysis of a host-parasite interaction. *Parasitology*, 59, 649–61.

SMITHERS, S. R. and TERRY, R. J. (1976). The immunology of schistosomiasis. *Adv. Parasit.*, **14**, 399–422.

SMYTH, J. D. (1972). Changes in the digestive absorptive surface of cestodes during larval/adult differentiation. In: Functional aspects of parasite surfaces. *Symp. Brit. Soc. Parasit.*, **10**, 41–70.

WEBSTER, J. M. (1975). Aspects of the host-parasite relationship of plant parasitic nematodes. *Adv. Parasit.*, **13**, 225–50.

WRIGHT, C. A. (1971). *Flukes and Snails*. George Allen and Unwin, London.

WRIGHT, C. A. and SOUTHGATE, V. R. (1976). Hybridization of schistosomes and some of its implications. In: Genetic aspects of host-parasite relationships. *Symp. Brit. Soc. Parasit.*, **14**, 55–86.